Thank you...

...for purchasing this copy of Numeracy Today for ages 7-9. We hope that you will find these 60 photocopiable pages helpful as part of your programme for the Numeracy Hour.

The sheets can be photocopied onto paper, card or overhead projector transparencies. Each sheet is preceded by an introductory page giving ideas, suggestions and answers where appropriate.

Please note that photocopies can only be made for use by the purchasing institution. Supplying copies to other schools, institutions or individuals breaches the copyright licence. Thank you for your help in this.

This Numeracy Today book is part of our growing range of educational titles. Most of our books are individual workbooks but, due to popular demand, we are now introducing a greater number of photocopiable titles especially for teachers. To find details of our other publications, please visit our website:

www.acblack.com

Andrew Brodie Publications

NUMERACY TODAY *for ages* 7 - 9 CONTENTS PAGE

The Hundred Square

The hundred square can be used:

... for counting on in tens

... for colouring in multiplication tables, (for example children can colour the three times table and see the pattern made - each multiplication table will make a different pattern so the pupils could have several copies of this sheet to enable them to show each of the tables)

... for shading all the multiples of 2 to show odd and even numbers

... as an aid to adding on or subtracting

... for higher ability children to find the prime numbers between zero and one hundred

Higher ability children, who are already confident with factors and the definition of prime numbers, can find the prime numbers between zero and one hundred as follows:

(i)   **Cross out** the number **1** as it is not prime.
(ii)   Leave 2 as it is a prime number but **cross out every multiple of 2** (4, 6, 8 ...)
(iii)   Leave 3 as it is a prime number but **cross out every multiple of 3** (6, 9, 12 ...)
(iv)   Leave 5 as it is a prime number but **cross out every multiple of 5** (10, 15 ...)
(v)   Leave 7 as it is a prime number but **cross out every multiple of 7** (14, 21 ...)

The numbers which are left uncrossed are all prime numbers.
This is called the sieve of Eratosthenes. Eratosthenes was a Greek astronomer who lived about 2100 years ago.

NUMERACY TODAY
© Andrew Brodie *Publications* ✓ www.acblack.com

The Hundred Square

1	2	3	4	5	6	7	8	9	10
11	12	13	14	15	16	17	18	19	20
21	22	23	24	25	26	27	28	29	30
31	32	33	34	35	36	37	38	39	40
41	42	43	44	45	46	47	48	49	50
51	52	53	54	55	56	57	58	59	60
61	62	63	64	65	66	67	68	69	70
71	72	73	74	75	76	77	78	79	80
81	82	83	84	85	86	87	88	89	90
91	92	93	94	95	96	97	98	99	100

The blank hundred square can be used:

... for children to make their own hundred square

... for marking on multiplication tables

... for children to make their own multiplication square

Blank Hundred Square

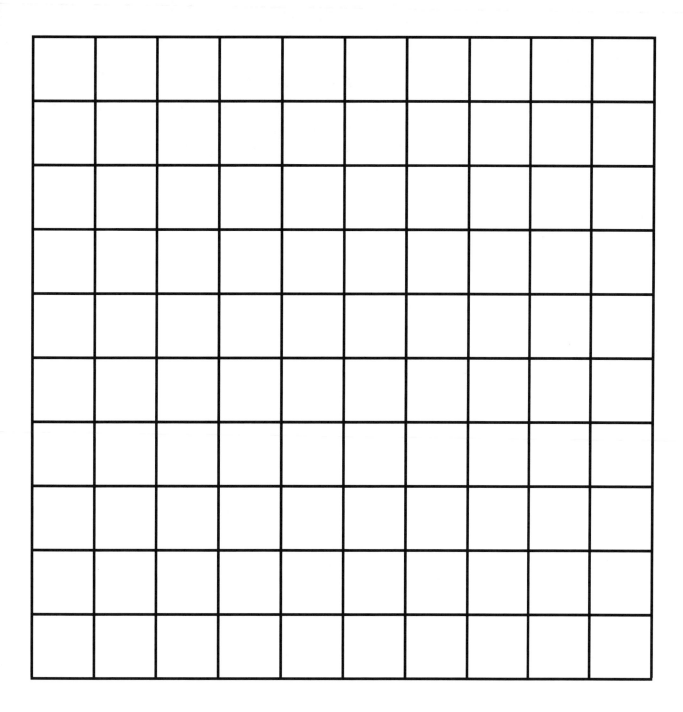

Number Tracks

Some children find positioning numbers surprisingly difficult, especially where counting crosses to 'a new hundred', such as ... 297, 298, 299, 300 ...

These number tracks encourage pupils to count forwards or backwards from given number-positions to identify positions of specified numbers. By completing tracks such as these, children are gaining confidence in counting 'big numbers' and in observing their properties.

Number Tracks

Name: Date:

Some numbers are missing from the number tracks shown below.

(a)

| 118 | 119 | 120 | 121 | 122 | | | | | | | |

Write the number 126 in the correct place on the track.

(b)

| | 75 | 76 | 77 | 78 | | | | | | | |

Write the number 84 in the correct place on the track.

(c)
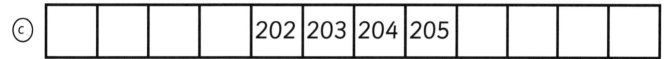
| | | | | 202 | 203 | 204 | 205 | | | | |

Write the numbers 199 and 209 in the correct places on the track.

(d)

| | | | | | | | | | 401 | 402 | 403 |

Write the numbers 393 and 395 in the correct places on the track.

(e)

| 289 | | | | | | | | | | | 300 |

Write the numbers 295 and 298 in the correct places on the track.

(f)
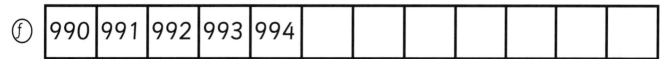
| 990 | 991 | 992 | 993 | 994 | | | | | | | |

Write the number 1000 in the correct place on the track.

Number Lines (1)

Every pupil needs access to a clear number line. You may wish to enlarge sheet 4 when copying it. It can be used to create class number lines to be shown in several places around the classroom or to make number lines for individual pupils. As you can see, we have shown the 10 at the end of the first line and at the start of the second line so that you can overlap them to create a longer number line. By repeating the overlaps on each line you can create a number line from 0 to 50 if you wish.

These number lines can be used for so many things:

... you could ask the children to start on the number 7 and jump 4 to 11, then to start on 17 and jump 4, then start on 27 and jump 4. Do they notice that adding a 4 to a number with a unit value of 7 always produces an answer with a unit value of 1?
Try the same thing with jumps of 8 or 6 or 9, etc

... you could ask them to start on 6 and to keep making jumps of 5. Do they notice that the units value keeps alternating between 6 and 1?

... you could ask them to start on 2 and keep jumping in twos. Do they notice that the answers are always even numbers?

... you could ask them to start on 1 and keep jumping in twos. Do they notice that the answers are always odd numbers?

... you could ask them to start on 31 and make jumps of specific numbers backwards.

There are many other examples where patterns can be found. Number lines often help children to see patterns which they can transfer into their mental work.

0 1 2 3 4 5 6 7 8 9 10

10 11 12 13 14 15 16 17 18 19 20

20 21 22 23 24 25 26 27 28 29 30

30 31 32 33 34 35 36 37 38 39 40

40 41 42 43 44 45 46 47 48 49 50

Jumping Tens

Adding on tens quickly is an important skill. Pupils who are confident with this skill are able to complete mentally more complicated additions such as 22 + 17. They realise quickly that 22 + 10 is 32, then simply add the 7 to make 39.

By using the 'jumping tens' method, many pupils find logic in the addition of ten which crosses from the nineties into the hundreds. A question such as 93 + 10 is far easier when seen on a number line like the one in question d on the page opposite.

The answers are as follows:

(b) I started at 71 . I made 2 jumps of ten. I landed at 81 and 91 .

(c) I started at 29 . I made 3 jumps of ten. I landed at 39 , 49 and 59 .

(d) I started at 91 . I made 3 jumps of ten. I landed at 101 , 111 and 121 .

Discussion of these questions can reinforce pupils' awareness of the process of adding ten. For example, in looking at question (a), you could encourage pupils to say:

'forty-three add ten equals fifty-three';

'fifty-three add ten equals sixty-three';

'sixty-three add ten equals seventy-three'.

Some children will need explicit guidance in recognising that when a ten is added the units value remains unchanged.

All the number lines shown can be used for other questions.

Jumping Tens

Name: Date:

Make jumps by adding tens on each of the number-lines below.
Draw arrows to make the jumps and draw a ring around each number you land on. The first one is done for you to show you what to do.

start here

42 43 44 45 46 47 48 49 50 51 52 53 54 55 56 57 58 59 60 61 62 63 64 65 66 67 68 69 70 71 72 73 74

(a) I started at 43. I made 3 jumps of ten. I landed at 53, 63 and 73.

start here

67 68 69 70 71 72 73 74 75 76 77 78 79 80 81 82 83 84 85 86 87 88 89 90 91 92 93 94 95 96 97 98 99

(b) I started at ☐. I made ☐ jumps of ten. I landed at ☐ and ☐.

start here

28 29 30 31 32 33 34 35 36 37 38 39 40 41 42 43 44 45 46 47 48 49 50 51 52 53 54 55 56 57 58 59 60

(c) I started at ☐. I made ☐ jumps of ten. I landed at ☐ , ☐ and ☐.

start here

89 90 91 92 93 94 95 96 97 98 99 100 101 102 103 104 105 106 107 108 109 110 111 112 113 114 115 116 117 118 119 120 121

(d) I started at ☐. I made ☐ jumps of ten. I landed at ☐ , ☐ and ☐.

Jumping Tens Backwards

Like making jumps of ten forwards, observing the effect of jumping ten backwards is of crucial importance to children. Many children have simply not noticed yet that subtracting ten only affects the numeral in the tens column:

86 – 10 produces the answer 76

76 – 10 produces the answer 66

66 – 10 produces the answer 56

etc.

When completing this sheet, the patterns emerging need to be discussed with the pupils. They can then be given quick mental work such as:

'seventy-nine subtract ten'

'forty-seven take away ten'

'eighty-three minus ten'

'ten less than sixty-four'

'one hundred and thirteen minus ten'

'two hundred and four take away ten'

You may need to use the number lines on sheet 7 to help pupils to visualise questions such as 'one hundred and thirteen minus ten' and 'two hundred and four take away ten'.

The answers to sheet 6 are as follows:

(b) I started at 98 . I made 3 jumps of ten. I landed at 88 , 78 and 68 .

(c) I started at 56 . I made 2 jumps of ten. I landed at 46 and 36 .

(d) I started at 119. I made 3 jumps of ten. I landed at 109 , 99 and 89 .

Jumping Tens Backwards

Name: Date:

Make jumps by subtracting tens on each of the number-lines below.
Draw arrows to make the jumps and draw a ring around each number you
land on. The first one is done for you to show you what to do.

start here

42 43 44 45 46 47 48 49 50 51 52 53 54 55 56 57 58 59 60 61 62 63 64 65 66 67 68 69 70 71 72 73 74

(a) I started at 72. I made 3 jumps of ten. I landed at 62, 52 and 42.

start here

67 68 69 70 71 72 73 74 75 76 77 78 79 80 81 82 83 84 85 86 87 88 89 90 91 92 93 94 95 96 97 98 99

(b) I started at ☐. I made ☐ jumps of ten. I landed at ☐, ☐ and ☐.

start here

28 29 30 31 32 33 34 35 36 37 38 39 40 41 42 43 44 45 46 47 48 49 50 51 52 53 54 55 56 57 58 59 60

(c) I started at ☐. I made ☐ jumps of ten. I landed at ☐ and ☐.

start here

89 90 91 92 93 94 95 96 97 98 99 100 101 102 103 104 105 106 107 108 109 110 111 112 113 114 115 116 117 118 119 120 121

(d) I started at ☐. I made ☐ jumps of ten. I landed at ☐, ☐ and ☐.

All the number lines on sheet 7 'cross the hundred', i.e. the numbers move from the nineties to the lower part of the next hundred.

You can use them to:

… show the effect of adding in jumps of ten

… show the effect of subtracting in jumps of ten

… point out the even numbers by circling multiples of two

… point out the odd numbers

… make jumps of five by adding or subtracting

… etc

Some pupils will gain particular benefit from working with number lines g and h. You can ask them to label specific numbers on the lines and to make jumps of certain sizes. Practice on these lines will help them with reading rulers, scales, thermometers and other calibrated measuring instruments.

Number Lines (2)

Name: Date:

(a)

89 90 91 92 93 94 95 96 97 98 99 100 101 102 103 104 105 106 107 108 109 110 111 112 113 114 115 116 117 118 119 120 121

(b)

182 183 184 185 186 187 188 189 190 191 192 193 194 195 196 197 198 199 200 201 202 203 204 205 206 207 208 209 210 211 212 213 214

(c)

391 392 393 394 395 396 397 398 399 400 401 402 403 404 405 406 407 408 409 410 411 412 413 414 415 416 417 418 419 420 421 422 423

(d)

679 680 681 682 683 684 685 686 687 688 689 690 691 692 693 694 695 696 697 698 699 700 701 702 703 704 705 706 707 708 709 710 711

(e)

284 285 286 287 288 289 290 291 292 293 294 295 296 297 298 299 300 301 302 303 304 305 306 307 308 309 310 311 312 313 314 315 316

(f)

792 793 794 795 796 797 798 799 800 801 802 803 804 805 806 807 808 809 810 811 812 813 814 815 816 817 818 819 820 821 822 823 824

(g)

90 92 94 96 98 100 102 104 106 108 110 112 114 116 118 120 122

(h)

90   100   110   120

Counting large numbers of objects can be quite challenging.

For question a:

Encourage the children to estimate the total number of aeroplanes first.
They should then count them in any way that they like.
Finally they should count them by drawing rings around groups of five.

Did they get the same result each time?
Which do they think is the most reliable method of finding the total?

They can now try the other sets of pictures by estimating, counting and then counting by arranging them in groups of 5 or 10.

Answers: (a) 39   (b) 48   (c) 53   (d) 41

Obviously it would be a good idea for children to try similar exercises with physical objects instead of pictures. They could count exercise books, pencils, buttons, etc, by putting them into groups of five or ten.

Counting by Grouping

Name: Date:

(a)

Estimate the number of aeroplanes shown

here and write your estimate in this box: ☐

Now count the aeroplanes and write your answer: ☐

Draw rings around groups of five aeroplanes.
Count up in fives then add on any aeroplanes left over.

How many did you find this time: ☐   Were all your answers the same?

(b)

How many pencils are there? ☐

(c)

How many flowers are there? ☐

(d)

How many arrows are there? ☐

5x5 Number Squares

Like other number squares the 5x5 square can be used to show patterns which can help children develop skills in mental arithmetic.

There are many combinations of activities which pupils can do:

They can start at one and count on in threes, colouring the numbers they arrive at:

1	2	3	4	5
6	7	8	9	10
11	12	13	14	15
16	17	18	19	20
21	22	23	24	25

They could start at two or three and count on in threes.

This square shows the pattern from starting at two:
Are the same number of squares covered as when we started at one?

1	2	3	4	5
6	7	8	9	10
11	12	13	14	15
16	17	18	19	20
21	22	23	24	25

They could start at one or two and count on in twos.

This square shows the pattern from starting at two:

1	2	3	4	5
6	7	8	9	10
11	12	13	14	15
16	17	18	19	20
21	22	23	24	25

They could count on in fours.

This square shows the pattern from starting at two:

1	2	3	4	5
6	7	8	9	10
11	12	13	14	15
16	17	18	19	20
21	22	23	24	25

… they could make predictions of what would happen if the square went beyond the number 25 … if, for example, they start at two and count on in fours, would 29 be coloured? … Would 35?

NUMERACY TODAY
© Andrew Brodie Publications ✓ www.acblack.com

ABP

5x5 Number Squares

Name: Date:

1	2	3	4	5
6	7	8	9	10
11	12	13	14	15
16	17	18	19	20
21	22	23	24	25

1	2	3	4	5
6	7	8	9	10
11	12	13	14	15
16	17	18	19	20
21	22	23	24	25

6x6 Number Squares

Like other number squares the 6x6 square can be used to show patterns which can help children develop skills in mental arithmetic.

There are many combinations of activities which pupils can do:

> … they can start at three and count on in threes, colouring the numbers they arrive at

> … they could start at two or three and count on in threes

> … they could start at one or two and count on in twos

> … they could count on in fours or fives or sixes

> … they could make predictions of what would happen if the square went beyond the number 36 … if, for example, they start at four and count on in fives, would 38 be coloured? … Would 42?

> … they could compare the pattern of threes made on the 5x5 square with the 6x6 square. If they start on two and count on in threes will they reach the same numbers on both squares? When they see that they will, they could compare the patterns which their colouring of these numbers make.

Remember, every time children see a pattern in numbers their mental skills are being strengthened. It is important for you as a teacher to point out what they have learnt by encouraging them to say the facts observed out loud …

> '… I started on 2 and counted on 3 and I reached 5. 2 add 3 equals 5.
>   I kept adding on 3. 5 add 3 equals 8. 8 add 3 equals 11. 11 add 3 equals 14 …'

1	2	3	4	5	6
7	8	9	10	11	12
13	14	15	16	17	18
19	20	21	22	23	24
25	26	27	28	29	30
31	32	33	34	35	36

Name: Date:

1	2	3	4	5	6
7	8	9	10	11	12
13	14	15	16	17	18
19	20	21	22	23	24
25	26	27	28	29	30
31	32	33	34	35	36

1	2	3	4	5	6
7	8	9	10	11	12
13	14	15	16	17	18
19	20	21	22	23	24
25	26	27	28	29	30
31	32	33	34	35	36

Number Sequences

Many children enjoy sequences as they are rather like logical puzzles.

In the first five sequences on sheet 11 we have provided loops for pupils to fill in the pattern which they have found, as shown in the example at the top of the sheet.

The final four questions do not have the loop provided. With these questions the children should find the pattern but they should not record it; they should simply follow the rule of the pattern to find the missing numbers.

The answers are shown below:

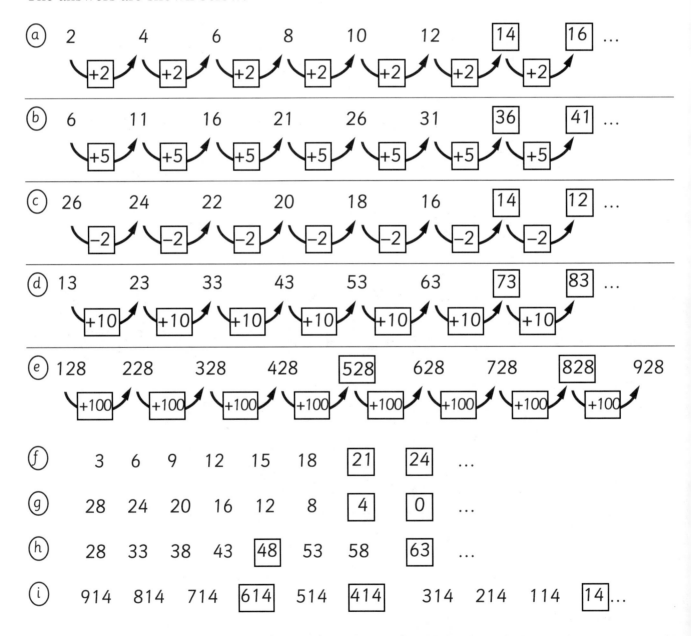

Number Sequences

Name: Date:

Look at this sequence of numbers:

4   7   10   13   16   19   22   ...

Now look at the pattern:

4   7   10   13   16   19   22   ...
  +3   +3   +3   +3   +3   +3

...so the next number would be 25 and the one after would be 28 and so on.

For each of the sequences below, find the pattern then find the two missing numbers.

(a) 2   4   6   8   10   12   ☐   ☐   ...

(b) 6   11   16   21   26   31   ☐   ☐   ...

(c) 26   24   22   20   18   16   ☐   ☐   ...

(d) 13   23   33   43   53   63   ☐   ☐   ...

(e) 128   228   328   428   ☐   628   728   ☐   928

Now try the sequences below.
In each one, find the pattern first so that you can find the missing numbers.

(f)   3   6   9   12   15   18   ☐   ☐   ...

(g)   28   24   20   16   12   8   ☐   ☐   ...

(h)   28   33   38   43   ☐   53   58   ☐   ...

(i)   914   814   714   ☐   514   ☐   314   214   114   ☐ ...

Try creating 3 sequences of your own...

Number Flashcards

Pupils need to be able to read and write numbers to at least 1000.

This sheet is designed to be photocopied onto card so that individual flashcards of a variety of numbers can be made. You may wish to enlarge the sheet on the copier.

You could simply ask pupils to tell you what number is shown on the flashcard which you hold up to show them or you could present them with a set of the cards and ask them to find a particular number.

Some of the numbers feature the same digits; 139, 319 and 391 for example. You could ask children to find other numbers using the three digits 1, 3 and 9 then to put all the numbers they have found in order of size, starting with the smallest or starting with the biggest.

Four of the numbers are consecutive (588, 589, 590, 591). You could ask the children to find the four consecutive numbers, i.e. the four numbers which follow one after another without a number between them. How long does it take the children to find them? Can they say the names of these numbers?

Five of the numbers have exactly 100 between them (574, 674, 774, 874, 974). Can the children find the five numbers? Can they name them?

The cards can be used by a child 'caller' in a bingo-style game; the four other players would use the game-cards on sheet 13. This gives plenty of practice in identifying numbers in an entertaining way.

Number Flashcards

38	57	86	99	107
116	139	172	202	222
227	243	272	319	331
391	400	414	440	455
463	487	499	517	533
547	555	561	574	588
589	590	591	603	612
625	637	649	652	669
674	681	695	702	733
774	789	814	840	874
900	929	956	974	999

Number Game Cards

This sheet can be photocopied onto card to create four bingo-style cards.

A caller picks at random from the numbers provided on sheet 12. The other players each have a game-card. As numbers on their cards are called, the players cover them with counters. The first player to have all her/his numbers covered is the winner.

Number Game Cards

86		139		331
	487	555		590
637	702		874	

57	172			272
	463	487		561
625	733			974

57	116		243	
	400	555		649
702		789		956

38		172	243	
	391	499		588
649		874		999

Numbers in Words

Children need to read and write numbers.

Sheet 14 gives practice in matching numbers to words, then in writing the words for the numbers provided.

Special features of spellings can be pointed out:

> … the letter u in four and fourteen, but no u in forty

> … the 'red' in hundred

> … the 'sand' in thousand

Numbers in Words

Match the numbers to the words. The first one is done for you.

37   four hundred and sixteen

678   three thousand, two hundred and forty

416   thirty-seven

523   forty-nine

195   seven hundred and sixty-eight

3240   six hundred and seventy-eight

768   one hundred and ninety-five

49   five hundred and twenty-three

Write these numbers in words:

218 →	
57 →	
729 →	
532 →	
1465 →	
999 →	
374 →	
483 →	
641 →	
806 →	

Place Cards

Sheet 15 should be copied onto card. The number cards should then be cut out to give this set:

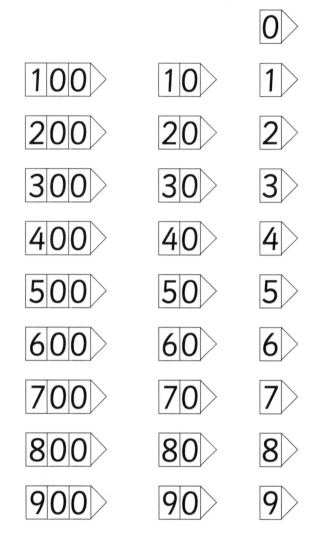

Children need to be able to see and understand the value of every digit in a number.

The number cards on sheet 15 can be used to create every number between 0 and 999.

Cards are placed over each other to create each number. For example, to create the number 642 we put the 40 card on top of the 600 card and the 2 card on the 40 card:

Place Cards

0 ▷

1 0 0 ▷   1 0 ▷   1 ▷

2 0 0 ▷   2 0 ▷   2 ▷

3 0 0 ▷   3 0 ▷   3 ▷

4 0 0 ▷   4 0 ▷   4 ▷

5 0 0 ▷   5 0 ▷   5 ▷

6 0 0 ▷   6 0 ▷   6 ▷

7 0 0 ▷   7 0 ▷   7 ▷

8 0 0 ▷   8 0 ▷   8 ▷

9 0 0 ▷   9 0 ▷   9 ▷

What's in the Box?

Children need full awareness of the value of each digit in a number.

In the number 642, for example, they need to realise that the digit 2 represents 2 units, the 4 represents 4 tens and the 6 represents 6 hundreds.

On sheet 16 we provide questions which can be used to test pupils' knowledge and understanding of place value. The pupils should have experienced oral work using the cards on sheet 15 or concrete apparatus such as plastic unit-cubes, ten-sticks and hundreds, or an abacus.

For speed of marking, the answers are provided below:

(a) 80

(b) 90

(c) 300

(d) 800

(e) 9

(f) 7

(g) 600   8

(h) 50   6

Note that for questions g and h, some pupils may give different answers. For example, in question h the missing numbers could be 30 and 26 - pupils who give answers such as these are not wrong and are demonstrating their mathematical ability. However, it could be pointed out to them that their answers are not following the pattern of the other questions on the sheet.

(i) 60

(j) 20

(k) + 200

(l) + 90

(m) − 300

(n) − 6

(o) − 700

NUMERACY TODAY
© Andrew Brodie *Publications* ✓ www.acblack.com

ABP

What's in the Box?

Name: Date:

Write the missing number in each box:

(a) 582 = 500 + ☐ + 2

(b) 795 = 700 + ☐ + 5

(c) 314 = ☐ + 10 + 4

(d) 873 = ☐ + 70 + 3

(e) 919 = 900 + 10 + ☐

(f) 137 = 100 + 30 + ☐

(g) 648 = ☐ + 40 + ☐

(h) 256 = 200 + ☐ + ☐

(i) 461 = 400 + ☐ + 1

(j) 828 = 800 + ☐ + 8

To solve each question below, you must make just one operation.

For example:

To make 519 into 819 the operation is + 300

To make 782 into 712 the operation is − 70

Now try these:

(k)   To make 604 into 804 the operation is

(l)   To make 604 into 694 the operation is

(m)   To make 312 into 12 the operation is

(n)   To make 596 into 590 the operation is

(o)   To make 863 into 163 the operation is ☐

Clock Faces

Sheet 17 consists of a set of ten blank clock faces. We have placed each clock in a box with a question letter so that …

> … you can photocopy the sheet, then write in each box a particular time that you want children to show on the corresponding face before photocopying the number of copies required for your class or group;

> … you can photocopy the sheet, then draw hands on each clock face before photocopying the number of copies needed so that the children can write the times in the boxes;

> … you can photocopy the number you require, then ask the children to enter a time of their own choice in each box by drawing hands on the clock and writing the corresponding time in words.

For other work involving clocks you may wish to use sheets 25, 32 or 57.

Clock Faces

Name: Date:

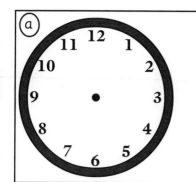 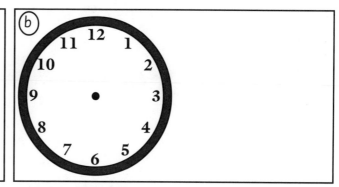

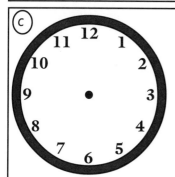 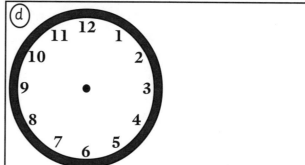

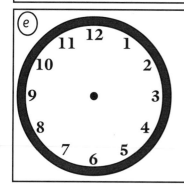 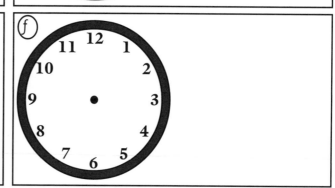

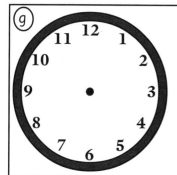 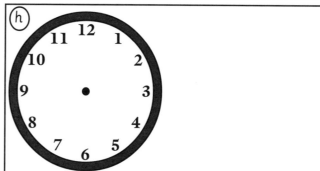

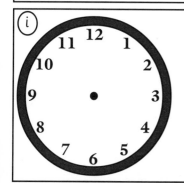 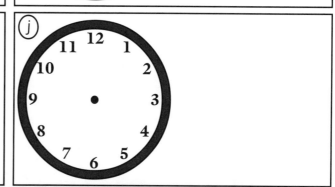

ABP ✓

Pupils need confidence in dealing with ordinal numbers, i.e. first, second, third, fourth, fifth …nineteenth, etc. Sheet 18 provides practice exercises for ordinal numbers.

Children could make their own bead patterns and discuss positions of beads.

The answers to sheet 18 are as follows:

(a) E   (b) J   (c) C   (d) M   (e) P

(f) black   (g) white   (h) white   (i) 9   (j) white

(k) H   (l) L   (m) 4   (n) G

Bead Positions

Name: Date:

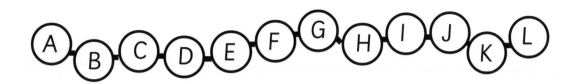

(a) What letter appears on the fifth bead?

(b) What letter appears on the tenth bead?

(c) What letter appears on the third bead?

(d) What letter would appear on the thirteenth bead?

(e) What letter would appear on the sixteenth bead?

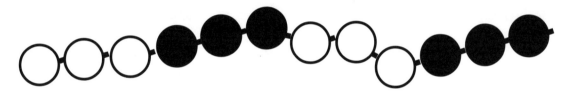

(f) Starting from the left, is the sixth bead black or white?

(g) What colour is the eighth bead?

(h) In this pattern, what colour would the fifteenth bead be?

(i) If there are 21 beads altogether, how many are black?

(j) What colour would the twenty-first bead be?

(k) What letter is on the fourth black bead?

(l) What letter is on the seventh white bead?

(m) How many white beads are after the third black bead?

(n) What letter is on the white bead which comes between the second and fourth black bead?

Sheet 19 is concerned with looking very carefully. Not only can it extend children's knowledge and understanding of numbers, it can also provide valuable practice in reading scales, thermometers, etc. (see sheet 7)

On lines a, b, d, e and f each spacing is worth 2. Lines c and g are easier in that the spacings all represent 1. Encourage the children to talk about the values of the spacings. They need to realise that the spacings are constant on each line but that they can vary between different lines, just like they can on different pieces of measuring equipment.

On line d you could ask the children to tell you the numbers which come halfway between 20 and 40, 40 and 60 then 60 and 80. Line e is similar. You could look back at line c and ask them to tell you which number comes halfway between 10 and 20. They should already have written 15 in the box, so move on to ask what number would be halfway between 20 and 30, then 30 and 40.

The numbers which pupils should have written in the boxes are as follows:

(a) 40

(b) 16 32 44 76

(c) 15 28 41

(d) 30 50 70

(e) 70 90 110

(f) 62 88 114

(g) 78 99 103

NUMERACY TODAY
© Andrew Brodie *Publications* ✓ www.acblack.com

ABP

Numbers on Lines

Name: Date:

Look very carefully at each number line. Write in each box, the number which should appear at that point on the line.

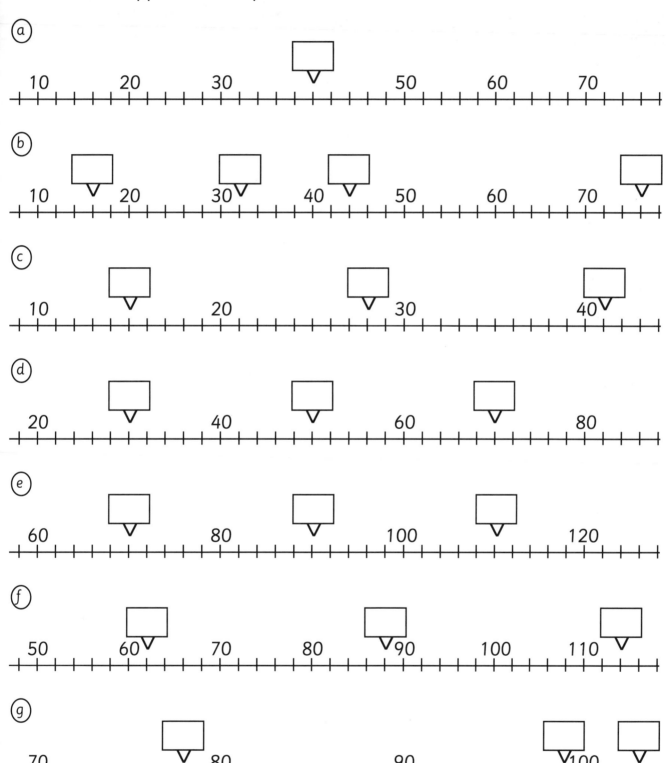

The ability to estimate is a very valuable skill. It helps pupils throughout their mathematics work; when dealing with any question they are able to realise whether their answer is sensible or not.

Estimating on simple number lines encourages greater understanding of number values.

In looking at question a on sheet 20, most pupils can see that the arrow is halfway along the line and that its position is therefore 5. This can help them when looking at question c where the arrow is a little bit further along the line and, again, if they are encouraged to compare question f with questions a, c and d, they should be able to estimate that the arrow is pointing to the 7 position.

Point out to the children that questions g to l are on a different scale. They may need considerable support and discussion in comparing the positions of the arrows. The arrow in question h is at the 20 position; by comparing h and j they should be encouraged to see that the arrow at j is slightly further along the line; by marking the halfway point on the line they may see that the arrow at j is half this distance. Similar comparisons can be made between the arrows at i and k.

The actual positions of the arrows are as follows:

(a) 5   (b) 1   (c) 6   (d) 9   (e) 3   (f) 7

(g) 50   (h) 20   (i) 70   (j) 25   (k) 75   (l) 99

Estimates

Name: Date:

Estimate the number which each arrow points to.
Write the number in the box.

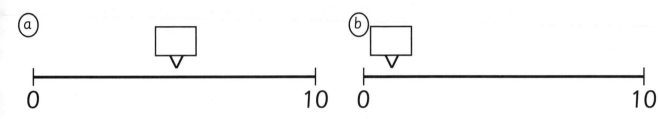

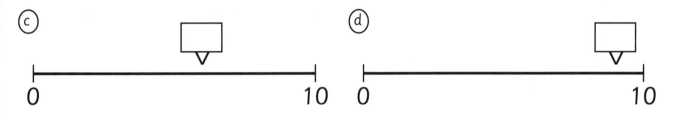

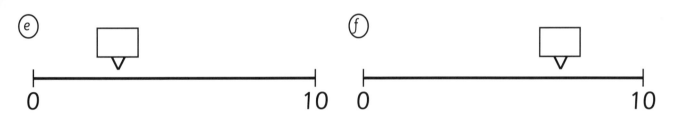

These number lines go from zero to one hundred:

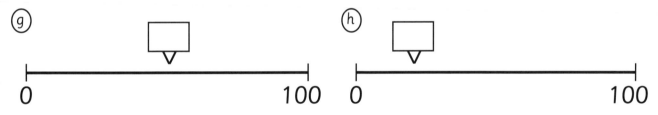

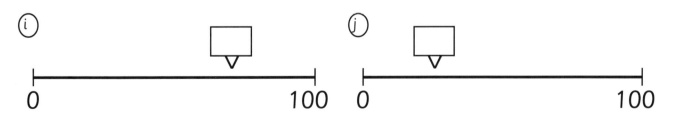

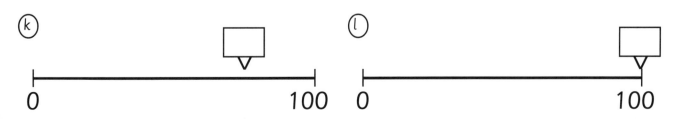

Rounding Numbers

Rounding to the nearest ten is an important aspect of estimation.

Sheet 21 provides a brief explanation of rounding to ten using a number line as a visual aid. The first four questions relate specifically to the number line but the later questions require the pupils to think for themselves either regarding the position of the number on the line or, if they are confident with number-work, the value of the number in relation to others.

The answers to the questions on sheet 21 are as follows:

(a) 30 (b) 40 (c) 70 (d) 80

(e) 50 (f) 50

(g) 80 (h) 70

(i) 100 (j) 30

(k) 50 (l) 90

(m) 80 (n) 10

(o) 20 (p) 20

Rounding Numbers

Name: Date:

The number line is marked in tens:

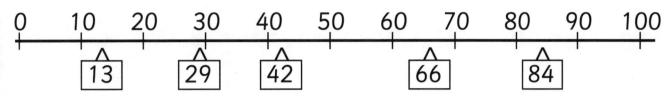

Number 13 is marked by an arrow. We can see that it is closer to 10 than 20 so we say that ...

... 13 is 10 rounded to the nearest ten.

Look at the number line to help you to complete these statements:

(a)   29 is ☐ rounded to the nearest ten.

(b)   42 is ☐ rounded to the nearest ten.

(c)   66 is ☐ rounded to the nearest ten.

(d)   84 is ☐ rounded to the nearest ten.

When a number is halfway between two tens, we always round up ...

... so 35 is 40 rounded to the nearest ten.

Now try these:

(e) 47 rounded to the nearest ten ☐   (f) 51 rounded to the nearest ten ☐

(g) 76 rounded to the nearest ten ☐   (h) 65 rounded to the nearest ten ☐

(i) 99 rounded to the nearest ten ☐   (j) 33 rounded to the nearest ten ☐

(k) 54 rounded to the nearest ten ☐   (l) 88 rounded to the nearest ten ☐

(m) 75 rounded to the nearest ten ☐   (n) 5 rounded to the nearest ten ☐

(o) 24 rounded to the nearest ten ☐   (p) 17 rounded to the nearest ten ☐

Rounding to the Nearest Hundred

Rounding to the nearest hundred is an important aspect of estimation.

Sheet 22 provides a brief explanation of rounding to the nearest hundred using a number line as a visual aid. The first four questions relate specifically to the number line but the later questions require the pupils to think for themselves either regarding the position of the number on the line or, if they are confident with number-work, the value of the number in relation to others.

The answers to the questions on sheet 22 are as follows:

(a) 100   (b) 200   (c) 300   (d) 500

(e) 400   (f) 200

(g) 500   (h) 600

(i) 700   (j) 400

(k) 900   (l) 800

(m) 500   (n) 600

(o) 300   (p) 700

Rounding to the Nearest Hundred

Name: Date:

This number line is marked in hundreds:

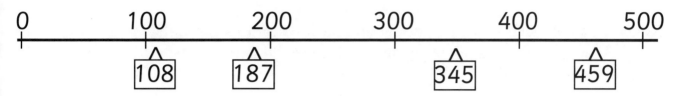

Look at the number line to help you to complete these statements:

(a)   108 is [   ] rounded to the nearest hundred.

    (b)   187 is [   ] rounded to the nearest hundred.

        (c)   345 is [   ] rounded to the nearest hundred.

           (d)   459 is [   ] rounded to the nearest hundred.

When a number is halfway between two hundreds, we always round up ...

... so 750 is 800 rounded to the nearest hundred.

This number line might help you when you try the questions below:

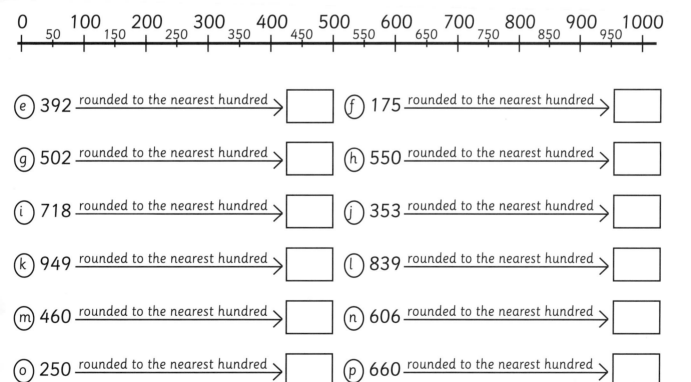

(e) 392 rounded to the nearest hundred → [   ]   (f) 175 rounded to the nearest hundred → [   ]

(g) 502 rounded to the nearest hundred → [   ]   (h) 550 rounded to the nearest hundred → [   ]

(i) 718 rounded to the nearest hundred → [   ]   (j) 353 rounded to the nearest hundred → [   ]

(k) 949 rounded to the nearest hundred → [   ]   (l) 839 rounded to the nearest hundred → [   ]

(m) 460 rounded to the nearest hundred → [   ]   (n) 606 rounded to the nearest hundred → [   ]

(o) 250 rounded to the nearest hundred → [   ]   (p) 660 rounded to the nearest hundred → [   ]

Fractions

Sheet 23 can be used simply as a discussion sheet where the teacher and pupils talk about the fractions shown, noticing the distinction between describing fractions of one whole and describing fractions of a set. Alternatively the sheet can be set as a worksheet where pupils write the answers to the questions on the sheet. You may find that the best use of the sheet is firstly for shared discussion followed by written completion by individual pupils.

The answers to sheet 23 are as follows:

(a) a half   (b) a quarter   (c) three quarters   (d) one third

(e) one tenth   (f) two thirds   (g) three tenths   (h) seven tenths

(i) four more small rectangles should be shaded

(j) two more small rectangles should be shaded

(k) three more small rectangles should be shaded

(l) one quarter of the set is ringed

three quarters of the set is not in the ring

Fractions

Name: Date:

What fraction of each circle is shaded?

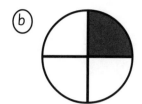 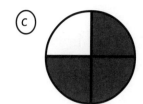 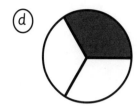

 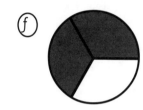  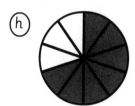

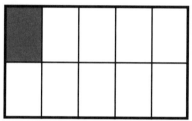 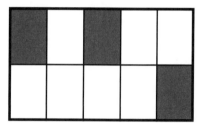 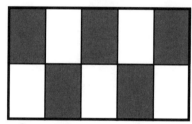

(i) One tenth of the large rectangle is shaded. Colour some more of the small rectangles so that one half of the large rectangle is shaded.

(j) Three tenths of the large rectangle is shaded. Colour some more of the small rectangles so that one half of the large rectangle is shaded.

(k) Half of the large rectangle is shaded. Colour some more of the small rectangles so that eight tenths of the large rectangle is shaded.

(l) Here is a set of footballs. What fraction of the set is ringed?

What fraction of the set is not in the ring?

Yet again, number lines are helpful in improving children's understanding of number.

Some children will find this sheet extremely easy and will complete it very quickly. Others will need considerable support. They should be encouraged to look very carefully at each line observing firstly where the 'whole ones' are, then where the half numbers are. These points should give them clues regarding the other marks on the line.

Ask them to count along line a: ' zero, a quarter, a half, three quarters, one.'

In a similar way, pupils should be able to count along line d:
' zero, a half, one, one-and-a-half, two.'

Line e: 'zero, a quarter, a half, three quarters, one, one-and-a-quarter, one-and-a-half, one-and-three-quarters, two.'

Pupils could do the same counting exercise on each of the lines. You can extend the activity by asking children to start at a particular point and to move forward or backward by a specific amount. For example, on line i or j pupils could start at number 7 and move back one-and-a-half; 'what point do you arrive at?'

After all the discussion exercises outlined above, pupils can complete the written work.

The numbers which pupils should have written in the boxes are as follows:

(a) $\frac{1}{2}$ (b) $\frac{1}{4}$ (c) $\frac{3}{4}$ (d) $1\frac{1}{2}$

(e) $1\frac{3}{4}$ (f) $\frac{1}{2}$ (g) $\frac{3}{4}$ (h) $1\frac{1}{4}$

(i) $3\frac{1}{2}$ $6\frac{1}{2}$

(j) $2\frac{1}{4}$ $5\frac{1}{2}$ $7\frac{3}{4}$

Fractions on Lines

Name: Date:

Look very carefully at each number line. In each box write the number which should appear at that point on the line.

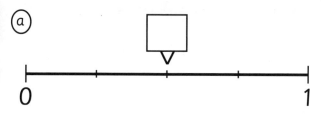

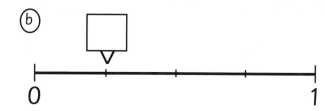

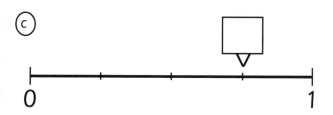

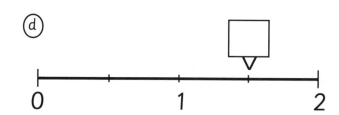

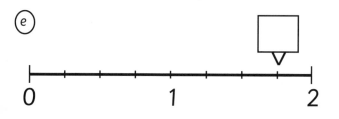

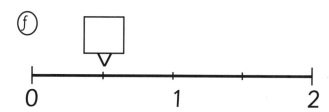

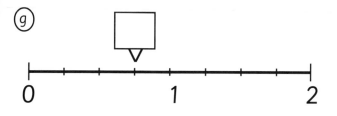

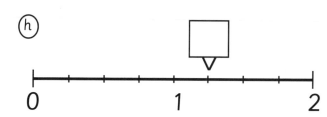

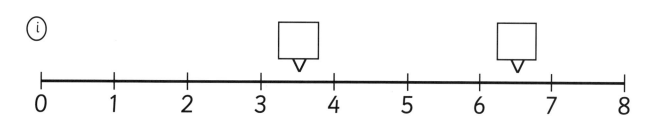

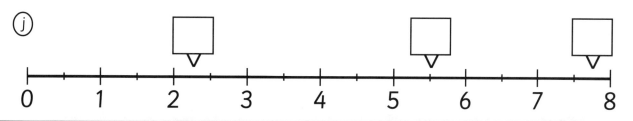

Fractions on Clocks

Many children have difficulties with telling the time. The link between fractions and clocks can be very valuable. Clocks can help pupils to understand fractions and fractions can help them to understand time!

When the time on a clock is not exactly on the hour, ask the child which hour the hour-hand visited last and which hour it is on its way to, then consider the position of the minute hand. Avoid saying 'when the minute hand is pointed to the three' or '…the six' or '… the nine'. Instead, encourage the child to see the clock face as a whole and to consider the quarter past, half past and quarter to.

For speed of marking the answers are as follows:

(b) quarter to five   (c) half past eight   (d) quarter to twelve

(e) quarter past eleven (f) quarter past nine   (g) approximately half past four

(h) approximately half past seven   (i) approximately a quarter to three

Fractions on Clocks

Name: Date:

What time is on each clock? Write 'half past' or 'quarter past' or 'quarter to'.
The first one is done for you.

half past two

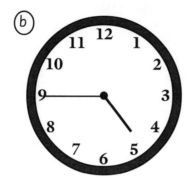

Write the approximate time shown on each clock below,
to the nearest half-hour or quarter-hour.

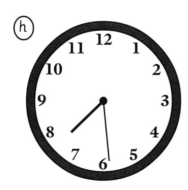

Addition Square

These addition squares provide valuable practice of number bonds to twenty as well as opportunities to examine number patterns. The 10 x 10 square will be easy to complete for most children and will create a useful 'ready reckoner' for them, enabling them to add quickly without having to use fingers or counters. Every time they refer to it reinforces their memory of particular bonds.

The mini squares at the bottom of the sheet can be used as speed practice and again will reinforce pupils' knowledge of number facts. Children can refer to the large square to help them in completing the mini squares. Encourage them to say the answer as they write it, using a complete number sentence, ie 'eight add six equals fourteen' or 'eight plus six equals fourteen'. Saying the complete sentence helps to store it into memory.

Answers to the mini squares, for speed of checking:

+	6	3	7	2
8	14	11	15	10
5	11	8	12	7
4	10	7	11	6
9	15	12	16	11

+	5	7	9	2
6	11	13	15	8
3	8	10	12	5
4	9	11	13	6
8	13	15	17	10

NUMERACY TODAY
© Andrew Brodie Publications ✓ www.acblack.com

ABP

Addition Square

Name: Date:

+	1	2	3	4	5	6	7	8	9	10
1										
2										
3										
4										
5										
6										
7										
8										
9										
10										

+	6	3	7	2
8				
5				
4				
9				

+	5	7	9	2
6				
3				
4				
8				

© Andrew Brodie *Publications* ✓ www.acblack.com

ABP

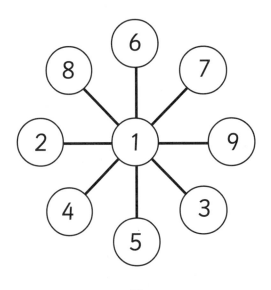

Teachers'
Notes for
Sheet 27

Children need to develop their reasoning skills and to gain confidence in manipulating numbers using their knowledge of number bonds. Sheet 27 provides three number puzzles for these purposes. Children should have pencils and rubbers available so that they can make attempts at solving the problems, then rub them out as they develop new strategies.

Possible answers to the questions on sheet 27 are as shown, but remember that there will be more than one way to set out the numbers:

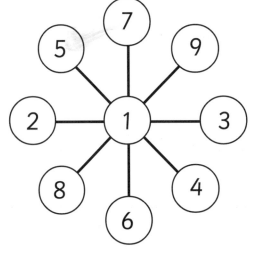

With this question, the children may need reminding that we are concentrating on the **joined** numbers... for example, the 4 is joined to the 3.

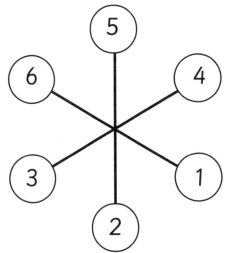

As you can see, the total is always 7.

Children may notice that the sum of the top number and the hidden number on a die always add up to 7.

Name: Date:

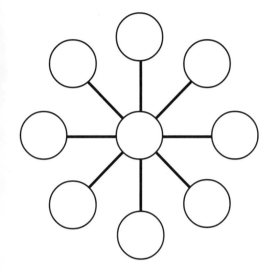

Write the numbers 1 to 9 in the circles so that three numbers in a line always add up to twelve.

Write the numbers 2 to 9 in the circles so that the difference between the numbers on the ends of each line is always equal to the 1 in the middle.

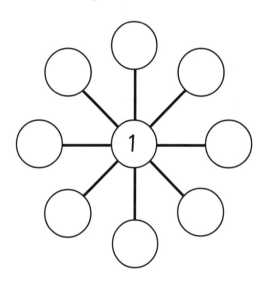

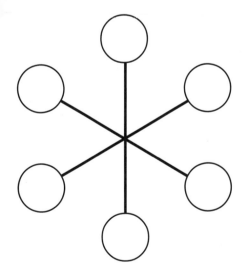

Write the numbers 1 to 6 in the circles so that the joined numbers always add up to the same number. What number is it?

Try rolling a die several times. Each time, add together the number which is showing at the top and the number which is hidden. What do you notice?

More Number Puzzles

On Sheet 28 pupils need to arrange numbers in triangles in accordance with given rules. As with Sheet 27 there may be some trial and error involved in the children's work but the more they do the more they will begin to see patterns and their work will be increasingly logical.

Possible answers to sheet 28 are as follows:

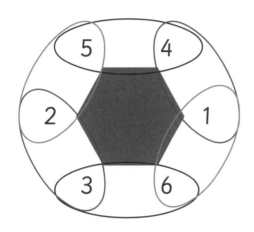

The first activity is designed to encourage pupils to follow instructions and produces an interesting pattern.

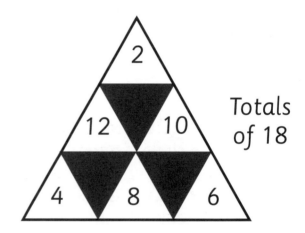

Totals of 18

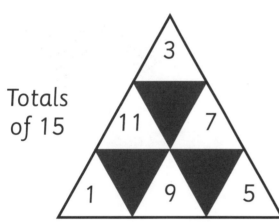

Totals of 15

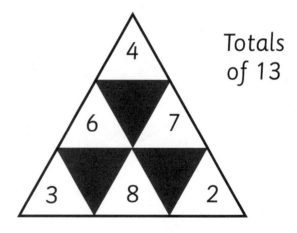

Totals of 13

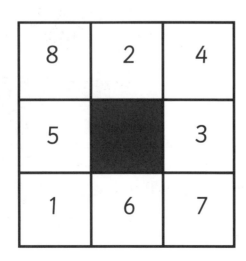

Totals of 14

NUMERACY TODAY
© Andrew Brodie *Publications* ✓ www.acblack.com

ABP

More Number Puzzles

Name: Date:

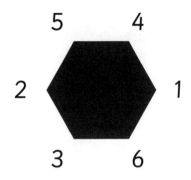

The numbers 1 to 6 are arranged around a regular hexagon.
Draw a red ring around the pairs of numbers which are next to each other and which total 7.
Now draw a green ring around the pairs which are next to each other and total 5.
Draw a blue ring around the pairs which are next to each other and have a sum of 9.

Write the even numbers 2, 4, 6, 8, 10 and 12 in the small triangles so that the numbers along each side of the large triangle add up to 18.

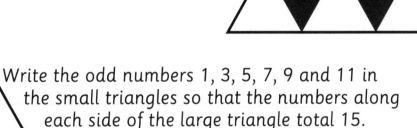

Write the odd numbers 1, 3, 5, 7, 9 and 11 in the small triangles so that the numbers along each side of the large triangle total 15.

Use the numbers 2, 3, 4, 6, 7 and 8 to make each side of the triangle total 13.

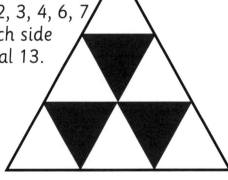

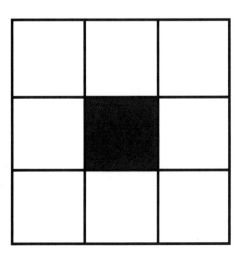

Write the numbers 1 to 8 in the small squares to make each side of the large square add up to 14.

Using a Ruler

Children need clear guidance in how to measure with a ruler. We often assume that it is an easy activity for them but watching what they do shows that some children start measuring from the very end of the ruler before the numbering starts and others start from the 1 mark. Pupils need to be shown a ruler. If it has inches on one side they need to be told that inches and feet are sometimes used but that we will be using centimetres and millimetres. They should be told that 10 millimetres are equal to 1 centimetre and so 5 millimetres are equal to $\frac{1}{2}$ centimetre and that, on this sheet, we will be measuring to the nearest half-centimetre.

The answers which pupils should have written in the boxes are as follows:

(a) 6 cm   (b) $7\frac{1}{2}$ cm   (c) 3 cm   (d) $3\frac{1}{2}$ cm

(e) 3 cm   (f) $12\frac{1}{2}$ cm   (g) 15 cm

NUMERACY TODAY
© Andrew Brodie *Publications* ✓ www.acblack.com

ABP

Using a Ruler

Name: Date:

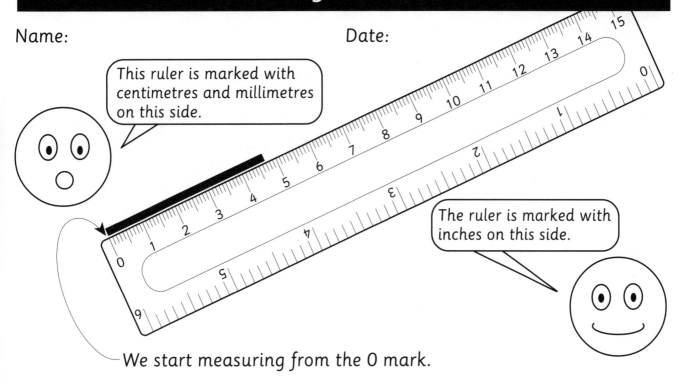

This ruler is marked with centimetres and millimetres on this side.

The ruler is marked with inches on this side.

We start measuring from the 0 mark.

You can see that the black line is more than $4\frac{1}{2}$ centimetres but not as much as 5 centimetres long.

We say that it is $4\frac{1}{2}$ centimetres to the nearest half centimetre.

We write the measurement like this: $4\frac{1}{2}$ cm   or this: 4·5 cm

Use your ruler to measure the lines below, to the nearest half centimetre.

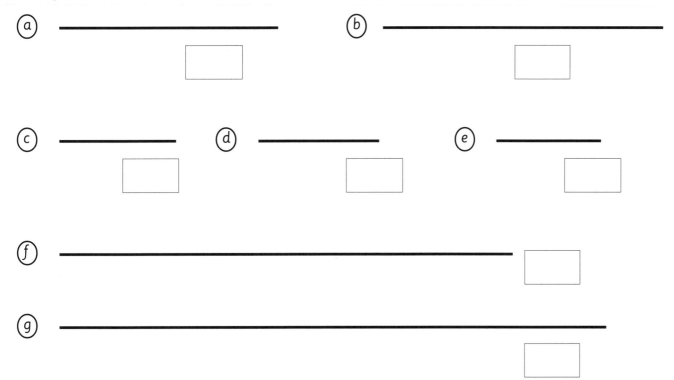

Reading Scales

Weighing scales come in a remarkable range of styles and formats. Many are now electronic but there are still a large number of 'old-fashioned' scales in use in kitchens, bathrooms and post offices. Sheet 30 presents children with pictures of kitchen scales to read. As with looking at a ruler or a number line, pupils need to be shown how to interpret the markings on the scales …

What numbers are present?

What units are we measuring in?

What markings appear between the numbered ones?

What do these markings represent?

The answers are as follows:

(a) 3 kg   (b) $5\frac{1}{2}$ kg   (c) $7\frac{1}{2}$ kg

(d) 3 kg   (e) 5 kg   (f) $1\frac{1}{2}$ kg

You may like to point out to the children that the answers to questions b, c and f can be expressed in different ways. For example, the answer to b could be written:

5·5 kg   or   5 kg 500g   or $5\frac{1}{2}$ kg

(g) $4\frac{1}{2}$ kg

(h) $\frac{1}{2}$ kg

(i) $5\frac{1}{4}$ kg

NUMERACY TODAY
© Andrew Brodie Publications ✓ www.acblack.com

ABP

Name: Date:

What measurement is shown on each of the scales,
to the nearest half kilogram?

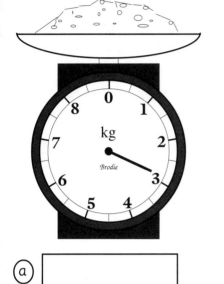  

(a) [ ]   (b) [ ]   (c) [ ]

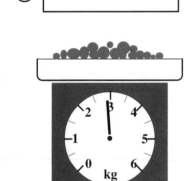 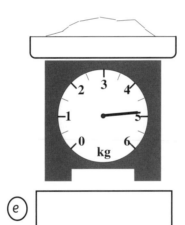 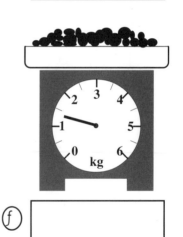

(d) [ ]   (e) [ ]   (f) [ ]

Draw items in the scale pans below.
Draw pointers on these scales to show the measurements provided.

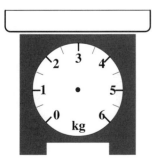 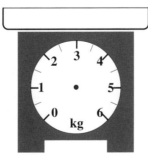 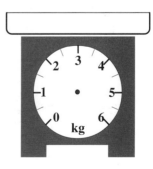

(g) $4\frac{1}{2}$ kg   (h) $\frac{1}{2}$ kg   (i) $5\frac{1}{4}$ kg

A Measuring Jug

Pupils continue to use their estimation skills, which they have learnt from number lines and from other measuring instruments, when they observe the quantity of liquid contained in a measuring jug. On the jugs shown on sheet 31 the measurements are all shown in millilitres. Children should learn that millilitres are often written as ml and that one thousand millilitres is equal to one litre (1000ml = 1l). As with other measuring instruments, close observation of the jug may be necessary to see how the units are marked on it.

(a) 600 ml   (b) 800 ml   (c) 500 ml

(d) 250 ml   (e) 650 ml   (f) 450 ml

(g) 300 ml   (h) 700 ml   (i) 750 ml

A Measuring Jug

Name: Date:

Write the quantity shown in each measuring jug.
Write your answers in millilitres (ml).

(a) [　　　　　]

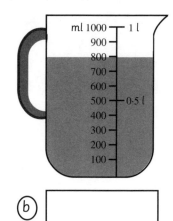

(b) [　　　　　]

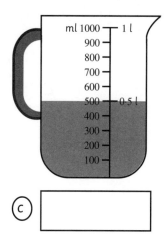

(c) [　　　　　]

(d) [　　　　　]

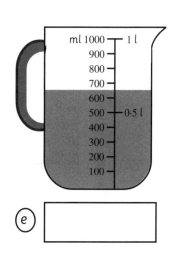

(e) [　　　　　]

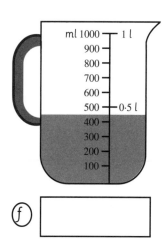

(f) [　　　　　]

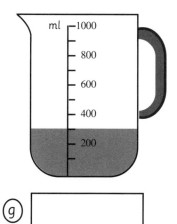

(g) [　　　　　]

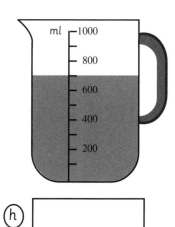

(h) [　　　　　]

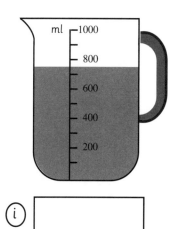

(i) [　　　　　]

Sheet 32 provides a set of clocks in both analogue and digital format together with times provided in writing. The pupils' task is to enter the appropriate times by

  … drawing in the hands of the analogue clocks;

  … entering the time in writing;

  … completing the digital times by drawing in the missing digits.

Clocks

Name: Date:

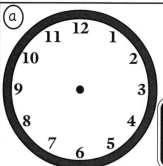

This is the time in writing.

half past two

This is called an analogue clock.

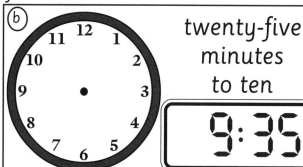

This is called a digital clock.

Fill in the missing information below:

(a)

five minutes past six

6:05

(b)

twenty-five minutes to ten

9:35

(c)

ten minutes to three

2:

(d)

twenty-five minutes past seven

:25

(e)

twenty minutes past two

:

(f)

:55

(g)

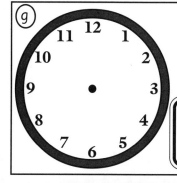

12:10

(h)

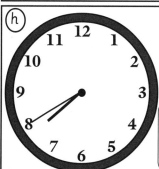

:

Two Dimensional Shapes

Sheet 33 provides abundant opportunities for discussion. The children can be encouraged to write down the name which best describes each shape. For example, a confident child should be able to state that there are four quadrilaterals on the sheet but the names 'square', 'rectangle' and 'parallelogram' provide the best description for three of them. Similarly, there are two hexagons and three pentagons but, in each case, only one of the shapes is regular. Of the two triangles one is regular but we use a special name for a regular triangle: an **equilateral** triangle, which means that the three sides are equal in length. In referring to the 'corners' of the shapes pupils should use the term vertices (singular: vertex). This sheet could be copied onto an OHP transparency for class discussion or it could be copied onto card then laminated and cut out. You may like to enlarge the shapes on your photocopier.

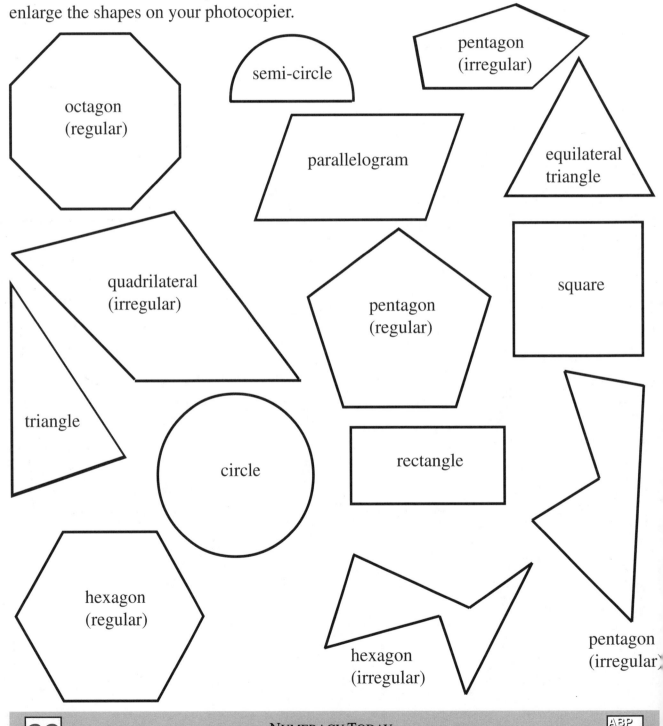

octagon (regular)

semi-circle

pentagon (irregular)

parallelogram

equilateral triangle

quadrilateral (irregular)

pentagon (regular)

square

triangle

circle

rectangle

hexagon (regular)

hexagon (irregular)

pentagon (irregular)

NUMERACY TODAY
© Andrew Brodie *Publications* ✓ www.acblack.com

ABP

Two Dimensional Shapes

Name: Date:

Write the correct name from the word-bank on or near each of the shapes below. Some names may be used more than once.

WORD BANK

pentagon   hexagon   circle   semi-circle   rectangle
square   quadrilateral   octagon   parallelogram   triangle

Line Symmetry

The pupils may be used to finding one line of symmetry. Sheet 34 encourages them to extend their knowledge of symmetry to deciding whether a shape has one line or two. They can use a mirror to help, placing the mirror to try to see, by combining the portion of the shape which they can still see on the paper with its reflection, an exact copy of the original shape. The solutions are shown below:

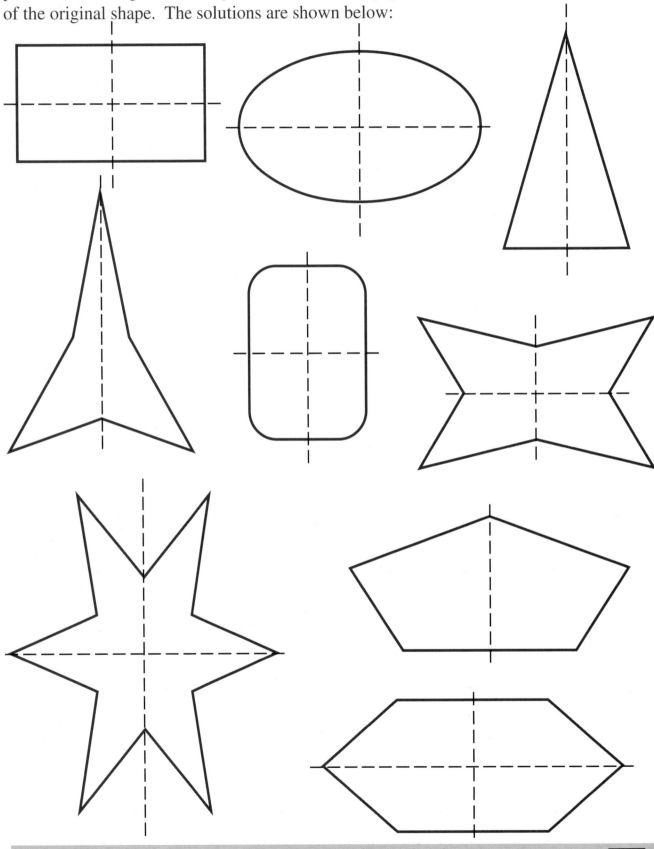

NUMERACY TODAY
© Andrew Brodie Publications ✓ www.acblack.com

ABP

Line Symmetry

Name: Date:

Some of the shapes below have two lines of symmetry and some have only one. Draw on the lines of symmetry. You can use a mirror to help you.

The pupils should be encouraged to draw the reflections carefully, observing that points of reflection should always be exactly the same distance from the mirror line as the original points.

The letters F G J K L N P Q R S and Z are not shown because they are not symmetrical.

The letters A H I M T U V W and Y have been drawn using a vertical line of symmetry and the letters B C D E O and X have been drawn using a horizontal line of symmetry.

Extension activities to sheet 35 would be to ask the children:

... which of the letters could have two lines of symmetry? (O and X)

... are any lower case letters symmetrical?

... are the letters shown on the sheet always symmetrical?
(Different fonts will produce letters that are not.)

Symmetrical Reflections (1)

Name: Date:

Complete each letter by reflecting the part shown, in the mirror line:

Which letters of the alphabet are not shown?

Why are these letters not shown?

_____

Which of the letters above have you drawn using a vertical line of symmetry?

Which have you drawn using a horizontal line of symmetry?

Positions on a Grid

Sheet 36 provides the early stages of finding grid references for geography and coordinates for mathematics. What is of most importance is that children develop the habit of giving the x-axis part of the position first and the y-axis part second.

By colouring the squares listed the pupils should find the word:

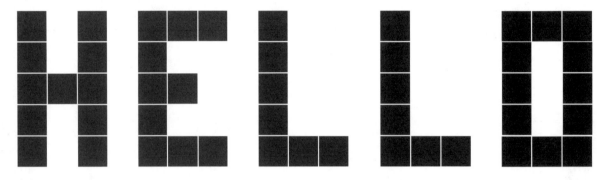

There is enough space left on the grid for pupils to write their own word and to state the positions of the squares which they have used.

You may wish to use the grid on the sheet for other activities. You could ask children to draw a picture using squares, then to give the positions of the squares to a friend to copy the picture without seeing the original.

The sheet can also be used for playing 'Battleships'.

NUMERACY TODAY
© Andrew Brodie *Publications* ✓ www.acblack.com

ABP

Positions on a Grid

Name: Date:

19																			
18	■																		
17																			
16																			
15																			
14																			
13																			
12																			
11																			
10																			
9																			
8																			
7																			
6																			
5																			
4																			
3																			
2																			
1																			
	A	B	C	D	E	F	G	H	I	J	K	L	M	N	O	P	Q	R	S	T

A square has been shaded on this grid. The position of the square is   B18.

Shade in all the squares with these positions:

B12 F16 K12 N14 T13 O12 G14 H16 N16 J15 D13 H12 C14 S12 R15

L12 J12 G16 B16 T12 S16 T15 D12 B14 R16 D16 F12 G12 P12 N13 R14

R12 F13 D15 J16 R13 B15 F14 T14 N12 D14 F15 T16 J14 N15 B13 J13

Now write a short word of your own and find the positions of the squares.

Compass Directions

Teachers' Notes for Sheet 37

Sheet 37 is completed using verbal instructions by the teacher or perhaps by another pupil. Instructions are given in the form of numbers of spots moved from the starting spot in a particular direction. Year 3 pupils should learn to work with compass directions North, South, East and West. Year 4 pupils should use North-West, North-East, South-West and South-East in addition to North, South, East and West.

For example:

… start at the black spot, move five spots in the south direction, colour this spot;

… now move three spots in the west direction <u>and</u> four spots in the south direction and colour this spot;

… move eleven spots in the north direction, colour this spot;

… move three spots in the west direction <u>and</u> two spots in the south direction and colour this spot;

… move five spots in the south direction and colour the spot you reach:

… now join the spots with straight lines;

… what shape have you drawn?

… is it a regular shape? (No)

… is it symmetrical? (Yes)

… how many lines of symmetry does it have? (1)

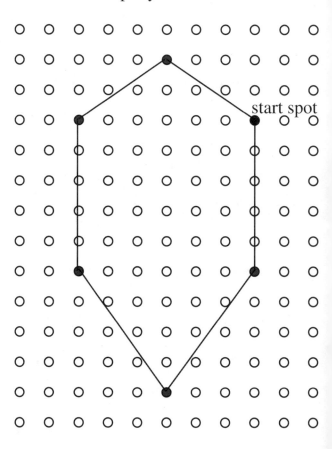

Many more instructions can be given and, of course, other shapes can be drawn on the same grid.

37

NUMERACY TODAY
© Andrew Brodie *Publications* ✓ www.acblack.com

ABP

Name: Date:

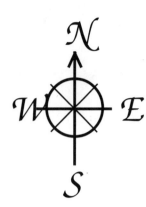

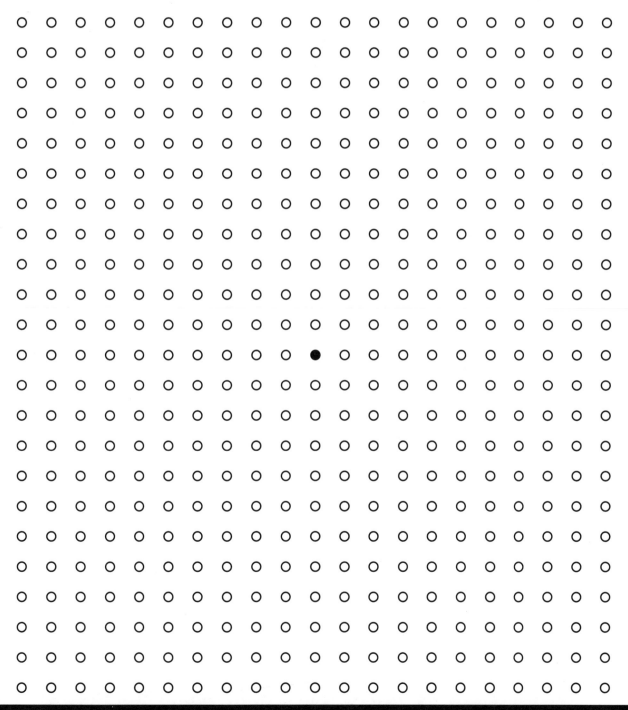

Sheet 38 provides several angles for pupils to measure with a right angle indicator.

The right angle indicator can be made from <u>any</u> sheet of paper by folding it carefully to create a straight line, then folding it again so that the first fold meets itself. Pressing the folds firmly will ensure that a right angle has been created.

The children need to be shown how to place their indicator carefully along one of the lines of the angle - this will help them when they move on to using protractors. They should be encouraged to realise that if they can then see the other 'arm' of the angle, the angle must be equal to or greater than a right angle but if they can't see it the angle must be less than a right angle.

The answers are as follows:

(a) less than a right angle

(b) greater than a right angle

(c) greater than a right angle

(d) less than a right angle

(e) less than a right angle

(f) right angle

(g) greater than a right angle

(h) less than a right angle

(i) greater than a right angle

(j) greater than a right angle

Greater or Less Than a Right Angle?

Name: Date:

Make a right angle indicator. Use your indicator to measure these angles to decide whether they are greater than or less than a right angle. If the angle is greater than a right angle, write 'greater' , if it is less than a right angle write 'less' and if it is equal to a right angle write 'right angle'.
Mark the angles in the same way as these three examples:

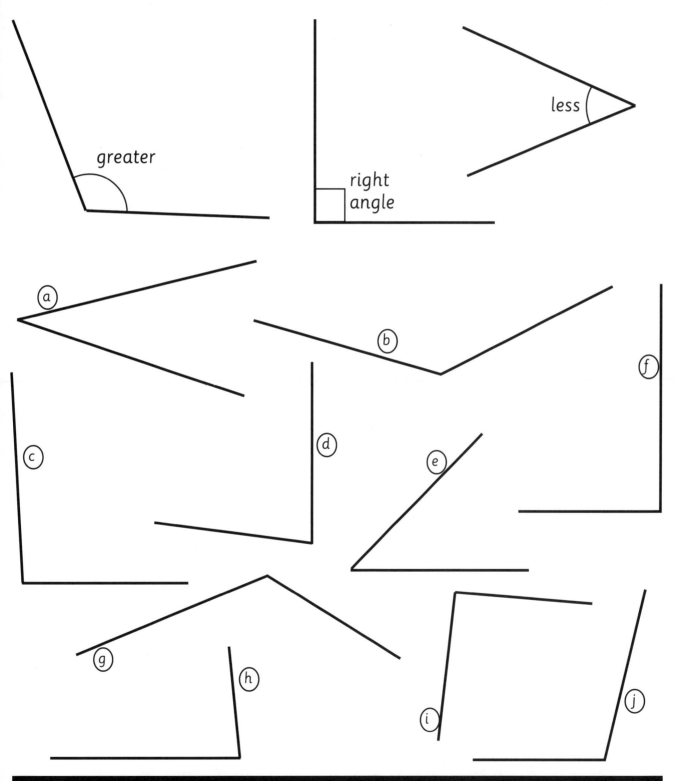

Simple Carroll Diagram

Teachers'
Notes for
Sheet 39

The Carroll diagram was created by Charles Dodgson of Christ Church College, Oxford. He was, of course, better known as Lewis Carroll. Sheet 39 provides the simplest form of Carroll diagram. The sheet can be photocopied to give every child their own copy to work on or it could be copied onto card to make a class set of Carroll diagrams.

Like the Venn diagram on sheet 40, the Carroll diagram is used for sorting numbers or classifying shapes according to specified criteria.

For example:

> … you could present the children with a set of the number cards from sheet 12 and ask them to sort them according to whether they are odd or not odd. ('not odd' numbers are obviously even numbers but we are here concerned with encouraging the pupils to consider one criterion only)

> … you could prepare a set of cards showing circles cut into fractions such as $\frac{1}{2}$ $\frac{1}{4}$ $\frac{2}{4}$ $\frac{3}{4}$ $\frac{3}{6}$ $\frac{1}{10}$ $\frac{7}{10}$ $\frac{5}{10}$ $\frac{1}{6}$ $\frac{1}{3}$ $\frac{2}{3}$ then ask the children to sort them into those equal to a half and those <u>not</u> equal to a half. For Year Four pupils you could also prepare fraction cards showing eighths (one eighth, two eighths, etc) , again asking them to find fractions which are equivalent to a half but then moving on to finding fractions which are equivalent to a quarter or to three quarters. Year Four pupils will also need cards showing the tenths 'family' , the sixths family and the fifths. The cards should include whole ones, ie four quarters, three thirds, etc. We have included a sheet of fractions to photocopy at the back of the book.

> … you could copy the shapes on sheet 33 onto card and ask the pupils to sort them onto the Carroll diagram as quadrilaterals or not quadrilaterals.

> … you could copy the shapes on sheet 33 onto card and ask the pupils to sort them onto the diagram as having line symmetry or not having line symmetry.

> … you could prepare a set of cards showing angles some of which are right angles and ask the children to sort them into right angles and not right angles.

NUMERACY TODAY
© Andrew Brodie *Publications* ✓ www.acblack.com

Simple Carroll Diagram

Name: Date:

© Andrew Brodie *Publications* ✓ www.acblack.com

This is the simplest form of Venn diagram and it is used in a similar way to the Carroll diagram on sheet 39. On the Venn diagram we again sort according to attributes being present or not present - numbers or items with the specified attribute are sorted into the circle; those without that attribute are placed outside the circle.

For example:

> ... you could use the number cards from sheet 12 and ask the children to sort them according to whether they are multiples of five or <u>not</u> multiples of five. This will help to consolidate the pupils' knowledge of the fact that multiples of five always end with a 5 digit or a 0 digit in the units column.

> ... you could prepare a set of cards showing letters of the alphabet and ask the pupils to sort them into symmetrical and not symmetrical. (Be careful to ensure that the font used does actually create some letters which are symmetrical as not all fonts will.)

> ... you could prepare a set of cards showing 2D shapes and ask children to sort them into symmetrical and not symmetrical. (Some shapes will have more than one line of symmetry - this will provide opportunities for discussion.)

> ... you could ask the children to write down the names of people in the class who travel to school by car within the circle and those who do not outside the circle. As with all the examples, appropriate language should be used, so there should be a title such as 'Travelling to school'; the circle would have a label, 'by car' and outside the circle would have 'not by car'.

> ... you could prepare a set of flashcards showing every number from zero to fifty, then ask pupils to sort into the circle all the multiples of two. This could be repeated for all the multiples of three, four, five or ten. Those who know the higher times tables could sort the multiples of six, seven, eight or nine from the set. As an extension activity you could ask more able pupils to sort the multiples of two, three, five <u>and</u> seven into the circle; those that are not multiples of two, three, five and seven are prime numbers. We have provided the numbers from 0 to 50 for photocopying, on the inside of the back cover.

Simple Venn Diagram

Name: Date:

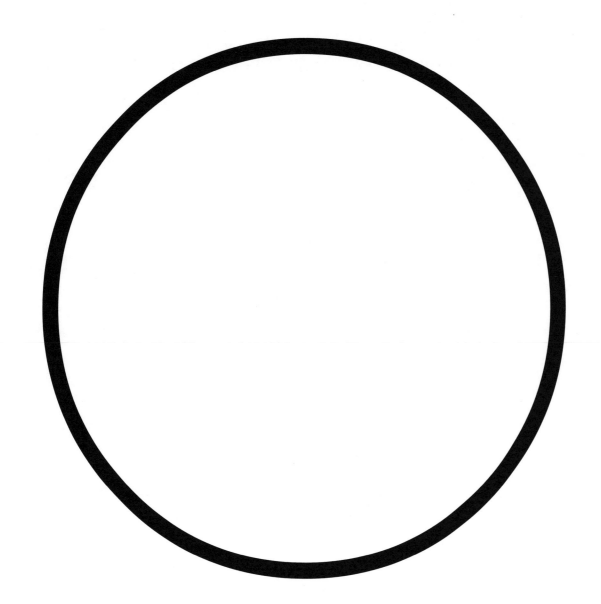

Handling Data: Favourite Fruits

Sheet 41 presents an opportunity to create a simple frequency table, then to use the data to draw a simple bar chart. Pupils should be encouraged to notice that the 'number of people' frequency axis is callibrated in twos rather than ones and therefore, for example, if they wish to enter a column of 9 people they will need to draw their line between the 8 and 10 marks. This axis can be considered as a type of number line and as such will be quite familiar to the children.

Questions regarding the data and the charts can be discussed with the pupils:

... which fruit is most popular amongst members of the class?

... which fruit is least popular as a favourite?

... should other fruits have been listed rather than just entered as 'others'?

... how many more people preferred fruit x compared to fruit y?

Pupils could use the same table and chart to enter data about least favourite fruits. This would highlight the importance of giving the chart an appropriate title. Comparisons could be made between the charts of favourites and least favourites. You may well find that the fruit which had the lowest number of votes for favourite fruit does not gain the highest number of votes as least favourite - the logic of this could lead to some interesting discussions with higher ability pupils regarding phrasing of questions in surveys.

Handling Data: Favourite Fruits

Name: Date:

Find out the favourite fruit, from the list shown, of everybody in the class. Record the totals in the table.

Favourite Fruit	Number of people
Apple	
Banana	
Orange	
Grapes	
Melon	
Pineapple	
Pear	
Others	

Now use your data to make a bar chart.

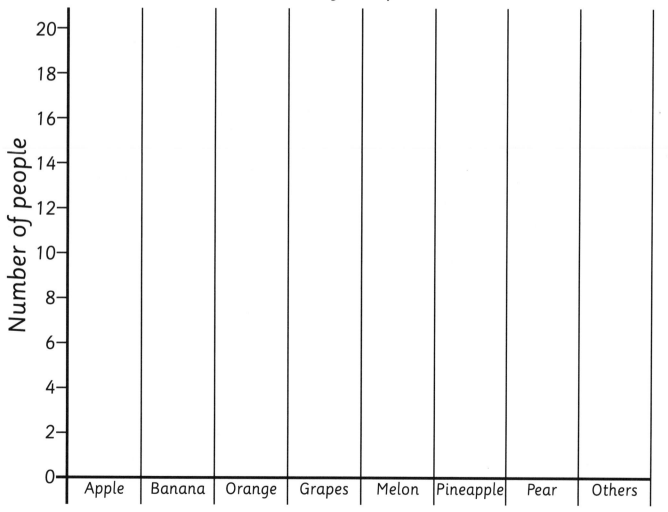

Favourite Fruits of People in Our Class

Handling Data: Telephone Calls

Pictograms are commonly used to display data graphically and clearly. It is essential for pupils to be able to interpret them. The biggest hurdle for children is always the understanding of the value of the symbols used.

Sheet 42 uses the example of telephone calls made to the school office over the course of one week. The telephone symbol ☎ represents two calls and, accordingly, the half-telephone ☎ represents one call.

As always, opportunities should be taken to increase pupils' understanding of the chart, and of charts in general, through appropriate discussion of questions.

For example:

> … why do you think Monday was the busiest morning for phone-calls?

> … if we wanted to do a similar survey of afternoons, at what times should we start and finish?

> … why would the data be different if we recorded it in August instead of January?

> … how many phone-calls were made altogether in the mornings of the week beginning 29th January?

Children could make their own pictograms of telephone calls received at home in the evenings or over a weekend. Actual surveys of phone-calls could be carried out in school for mornings, afternoons, whole days. Surveys could be carried out regarding phone-calls made *from* the school - some pupils could extend the study by considering the costs of phone-calls.

Handling Data: Telephone Calls

Name: Date:

The school secretary made a note of the number of telephone calls to the school office every morning for one week. She drew a pictogram of the data.

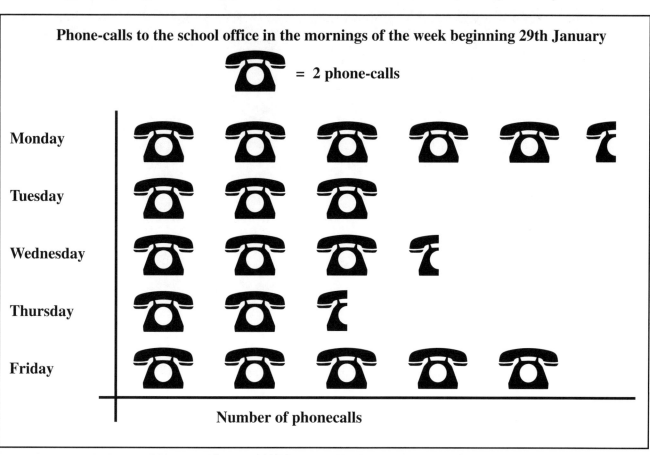

Phone-calls to the school office in the mornings of the week beginning 29th January

= 2 phone-calls

Monday

Tuesday

Wednesday

Thursday

Friday

Number of phonecalls

Use the pictogram to help you to answer these questions:

(a) How many phone calls were made to the office on each morning of the week?

Monday [ ]   Tuesday [ ]   Wednesday [ ]   Thursday [ ]   Friday [ ]

(b) Which was the busiest day of the week for phone calls? [ ]

(c) Which was the quietest day of the week for phone calls? [ ]

(d) How many more calls were there on Monday than Friday? [ ]

(e) How many fewer calls were there on 1st February than 2nd February? [ ]

Flashcards with Thousands

Year 4 pupils need to be confident and competent with four-digit numbers.

Sheet 43 provides a set of flashcards additional to those on sheet 12. They can simply be used as flashcards but the children could also be asked to try the following activites:

> … find all the cards which show multiples of a thousand.

> … find and name all the cards which have a zero in the hundreds column.

> … find and name all the cards which have a zero in the tens column.

> … find and name all the cards which have a zero in the units column.

> … find the five cards from the set which form an unbroken sequence of consecutive numbers. (4998, 4999, 5000, 5001, 5002)

> … find the card which is halfway between 7000 and 8000.

> … find the card which is halfway between 7000 and 7500.

> … find the card which is halfway between 7500 and 8000.

> … find the card which is 5000 less than 9999.

> … put all the cards in order when they have been mixed up.

There are many possibilities. Some can be combined with the Carroll or Venn diagrams on sheets 39 and 40, remembering that only one attribute can be considered. For example, you could ask the pupils to put all the cards which are multiples of 500 within the circle of the Venn diagram and to put those which are <u>not</u> multiples of 500 outside the circle.

1000	1016	1061	1275
1500	1802	2000	2317
2500	2713	2809	3000
3040	3403	3500	3777
4000	4500	4683	4836
4863	4998	4999	5000
5001	5002	5005	5500
5750	6000	6009	6161
6303	6500	7000	7250
7500	7750	8000	8500
8643	9000	9500	9999

Number Lines (3)

Year 4 pupils need to be able to give a number lying between two specified numbers. The number lines provide a clear representation of number values and the halfway point between two numbers is relatively easy to identify. However, some pupils will have difficulty with questions c, f, g and h and may need to be reminded of the need to carefully observe the value of each marking between the numbers provided.

For ease of marking, the answers to the first eight questions are as follows:

(a) 635   (b) 995   (c) 1005   (d) 2350   (e) 3050   (f) 1050   (g) 675   (h) 3445

Putting numbers in order is another valuable skill. Children need to learn the importance of reading instructions carefully as sometimes they will be asked to put numbers in order from smallest to largest and sometimes from largest to smallest. They should also be encouraged to read the numbers out loud.

The answers to these questions are as follows:

(i) 2314 2413 3124 3214 4132

(j) 5697 5769 5967 6759 6975

(k) 1038 3018 3081 3180 3810

(l) 9451 5941 5194 4915 4195

(m) 9277 7927 7792 2977 2797

NUMERACY TODAY
© Andrew Brodie *Publications* ✓ www.acblack.com

ABP

Number Lines (3)

Name: Date:

The half way point between two numbers is marked with an arrow on each of these number lines. Write the missing number in the arrow-box.

(a)
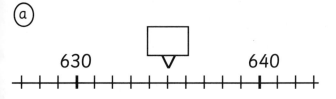

(b)
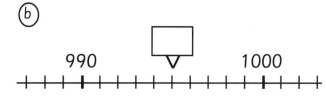

(c)
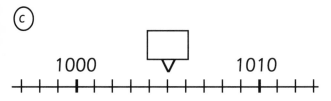

(d)
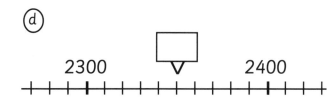

(e)
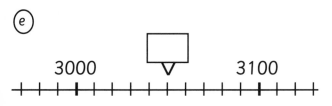

(f)
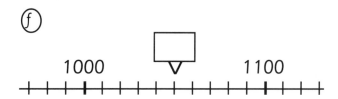

(g)
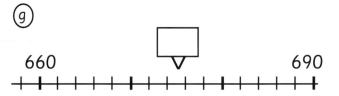

(h)
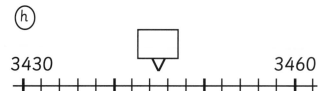

The numbers below need to be put in order from smallest to largest. You could try to imagine a number line to help you to decide the order.

(i) 3214   2413   2314   4132   3124
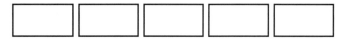

(j) 6975   6759   5769   5967   5697
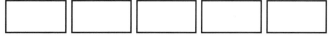

(k) 1038   3018   3810   3081   3180

Put these sets of numbers in order from largest to smallest:

(l) 4195   4915   5194   9451   5941

(m) 7792   7927   2977   2797   9277

Negative Numbers

Year 4 pupils can observe temperature callibrations on thermometers and realise that, on very cold days in winter, the temperature falls below zero. Thermometers provide an excellent introduction to negative numbers. In reading temperatures on a thermometer, children find it helpful to firstly locate the zero then to consider how far above or below zero is indicated by the liquid. In looking at the thermometers which show sub-zero temperatures, the children can count down from the zero. They should be encouraged to read the numbers as 'negative one', 'negative two', etc, although they will be accustomed to hearing weather forecasters referring to 'minus one', 'minus two', etc.

The answers are as follows:

a 2°C   b 1°C   c 0°C   d ⁻1°C   e ⁻3°C   f ⁻5°C   g ⁻11°C

h ⁻2, 0, 3   i ⁻6, ⁻4, ⁻1   j 0   k ⁻1, 1

l ⁻1   m ⁻3

Negative Numbers

Name: Date:

Write down the temperature shown on each thermometer. Not all of them show temperatures which are negative.

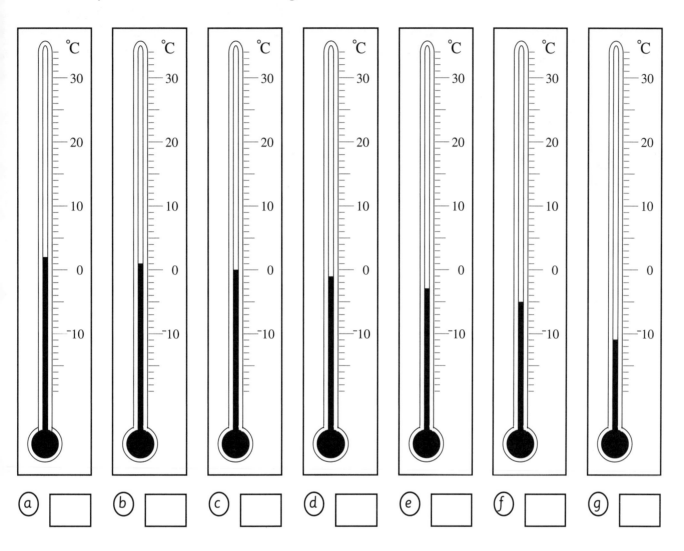

Write the numbers in the arrow-boxes on these sections of number lines:

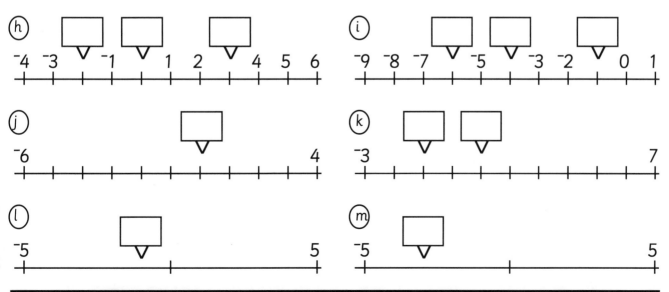

Decimal Fractions

Year Four pupils need to see the links between tenths expressed as fractions or in decimal fraction notation. The answers are as follows:

Amount shaded = six tenths = $^6/_{10}$ = 0·6

Amount shaded = three tenths = $^3/_{10}$ = 0·3

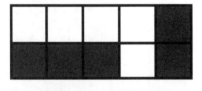

Amount shaded = five tenths = $^5/_{10}$ = 0·5

Amount shaded = four tenths = $^4/_{10}$ = 0·4

Amount shaded = seven tenths = $^7/_{10}$ = 0·7

Amount shaded = nine tenths = $^9/_{10}$ = 0·9

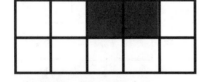

Amount shaded = two tenths = $^2/_{10}$ = 0·2

Amount shaded = eight tenths = $^8/_{10}$ = 0·8

NUMERACY TODAY
© Andrew Brodie *Publications* ✓ www.acblack.com

ABP

Decimal Fractions

Name: Date:

Complete each set. The first one is done for you.

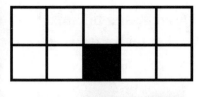

Amount shaded = | one tenth | = | $^{1}/_{10}$ | = | 0·1 |

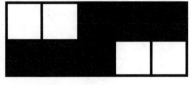

Amount shaded = | | = | | = | |

Amount shaded = | | = | | = | |

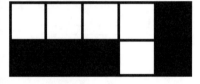

Amount shaded = | | = | | = | |

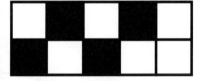

Amount shaded = | | = | | = | |

Amount shaded = | | = | | = | |

Amount shaded = | | = | | = | |

Amount shaded = | nine tenths | = | | = | |

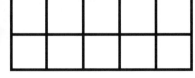

Amount shaded = | | = | | = | 0·2 |

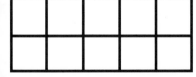

Amount shaded = | | = | $^{8}/_{10}$ | = | |

Number Lines: Decimals

Year 4 pupils will be accustomed to using number lines; learning to position decimal numbers on number lines will aid their awareness of the values of decimals. Some pupils initially have difficulty in understanding the value of whole ones in relation to decimals. In question h, for example, some may see the 2 as being the smallest number listed. It can be explained to them that the 2 could be written as 2·0 , which is two units and no tenths, and therefore the 2 is the largest number in that list.

The answers are as follows:

(a) 0·6   (b) 0·2   0·7   (c) 0·2   0·8   1·3   1·5   1·9   (d) 0·4   0·9   1·1   1·7   2·1

(e)

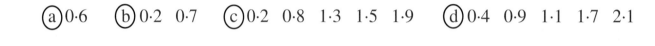

(f)   0·1   0·5   0·6   0·8   0·9

(g)   0·8   0·9   1·1   1·4   1·7

(h)   0·4   0·7   1·3   1·9   2

(i)   4   3·6   2·9   1·7   0·8

(j)   3·1   3   2·8   1·4   0·6

NUMERACY TODAY
© Andrew Brodie *Publications* ✓ www.acblack.com

ABP

Number Lines: Decimals

Name: Date:

Look very carefully at these number lines, then mark the missing numbers in the arrow-boxes.

(a)
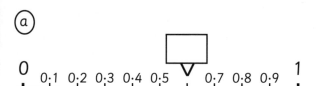

(b)
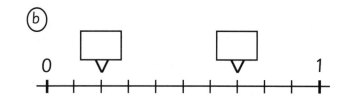

(c)
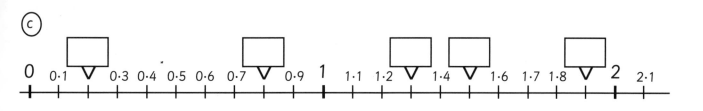

(d)
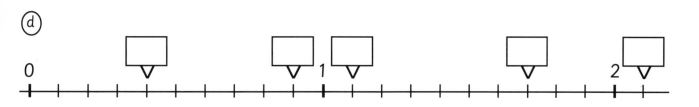

(e) Mark these decimals on the line: 1·7, 0·8, 0·1, 1·4, 2·1, 1·2, 0·9, 0·5

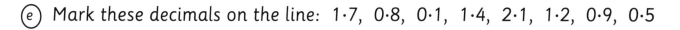

The numbers below need to be put in order from smallest to largest. You could try to imagine a number line to help you to decide the order.

(f)   0·8 0·5 0·9 0·1 0·6

(g)   1·4 0·9 1·7 0·8 1·1

(h)   2 0·4 0·7 1·9 1·3

Put these sets of numbers in order from largest to smallest:

(i)   3·6 4 0·8 2·9 1·7

(j)   2·8 1·4 3·1 0·6 3

Solving Problems: Shapes

Problem solving can cover all areas of mathematics. What is needed in each case is the appliance of logic. Sheet 48 provides some challenging problems with shapes. Children may need some support with the first one but from then on they can use the same logical steps in solving the others. All of the shapes give many opportunities for discussion. You may decide that working in pairs is the best method for all the questions. We *think* that all of the solutions are provided below but you may find more! Light shading with colouring pencils may help.

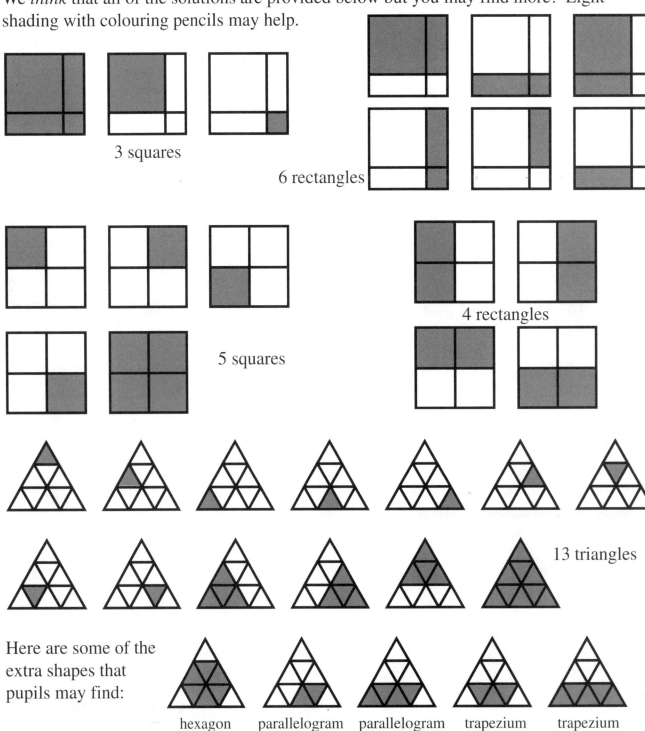

3 squares

6 rectangles

5 squares

4 rectangles

13 triangles

Here are some of the extra shapes that pupils may find:

hexagon   parallelogram   parallelogram   trapezium   trapezium

Other parallelograms and trapeziums can be found in different positions.

Please note that pupils do not need to know parallelograms and trapeziums until Year 6.

NUMERACY TODAY
© Andrew Brodie *Publications* ✓ www.acblack.com

ABP

Solving Problems: Shapes

Name: Date:

ⓐ

How many squares can you see? ☐

How many rectangles can you see? ☐

ⓑ

How many squares can you see? ☐

How many rectangles can you see? ☐

ⓒ

How many triangles can you see? ☐

Name any other shapes you can see:

These extra triangles are provided for you to shade parts in with coloured pencils to help you to find the answers.

What Shapes Can You See?

As with sheet 48, this sheet presents an interesting set of logic problems, this time based around just one picture. We recommend that pupils work with partners, to stimulate discussion about the shapes. You may also wish to set other questions about the picture, or invite the pupils to invent their own questions for others to answer.

hexagon

4 triangles

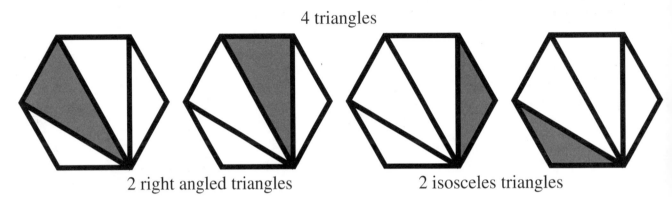

2 right angled triangles   2 isosceles triangles

3 quadrilaterals
(Note: pupils do not
need to know the
names kite or
trapezium until Year 6)

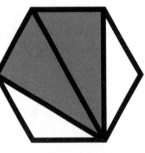

kite

trapezium

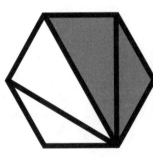

trapezium

2 pentagons

This line will produce
6 extra triangles ...

...this one is isosceles ...

... and this one is
equilateral.

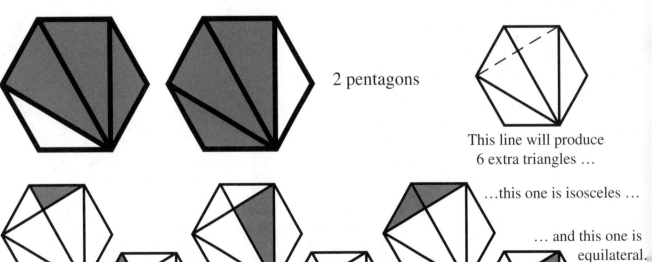

What Shapes Can You See?

Name: Date:

What is the name of the largest
shape you can see?

How many triangles can you see?

Is there anything special
about the triangles?

How many quadrilaterals
can you see?

Can you see any other shapes?

How could you make six extra
triangles just by drawing one
more line?

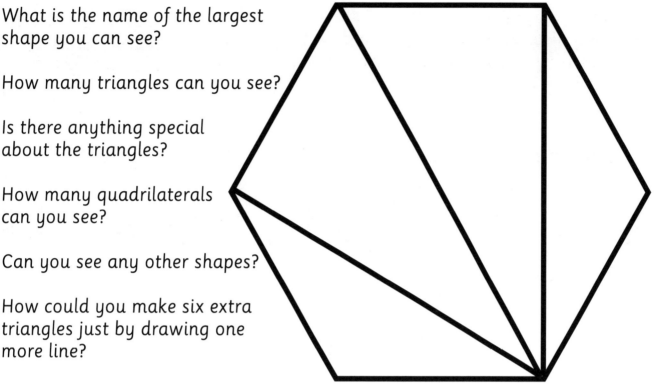

Here are some extra copies of the picture so that you can draw on them to
help find the answers to the questions:

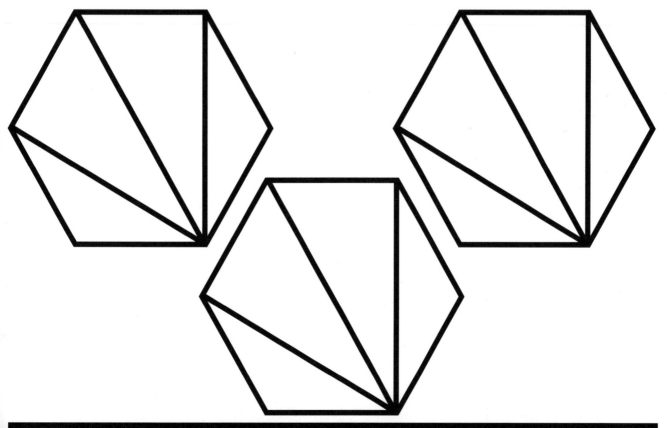

Sheet 50 requires pupils to use a ruler with more accuracy than is required on sheet 29.

For questions f and g the pupils will need to use a piece of thread to follow the lines then measure the thread with a ruler.

The answers are as follows:

(a) 9 cm 4 mm   94 mm

(b) 7 cm 8 mm   78 mm

(c) 8 cm 1 mm   81 mm

(d) 9 cm 1 mm   91 mm

(e) 9 cm   90 mm

(f) 7 cm 7 mm   77 mm   (allow answers between 75 mm and 79 mm)

(g) 14 cm 9 mm   149 mm   (allow answers between 146 mm and 152 mm)

Length to the Nearest Millimetre

Name: Date:

The black line is nearly 6¹/₂ centimetres long.
To be more accurate we can see that it is 6 centimetres and 3 millimetres long.
Every centimetre is 10 millimetres long so we can say that the line is:

6 cm 3 mm   or   63 mm

Measure the length of each line to the nearest millimetre.
Write your answer in two ways.

(a)

(b)

(c)

(d)

(e)

(f)

(g)

Using Measuring Equipment

Sheet 51 provides a development from sheets 30 and 31. The measuring cylinders are now to be read to the nearest 10ml. The three bathroom scales questions are provided as an extra challenge. Pupils will need to look very carefully at the calibration of the scales when Sarah was using them; once they have answered that question the others will be possible. Note, of course, that question o would be impossible if we did not already know the calibration of the scales from the previous two questions.

Clearly, much practical work would be useful alongside the work on this sheet. Children will observe differences in calibration methods on real apparatus such as bathroom scales and will become more adept at using them confidently.

The answers are as follows:

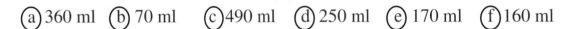

(a) 360 ml   (b) 70 ml   (c) 490 ml   (d) 250 ml   (e) 170 ml   (f) 160 ml

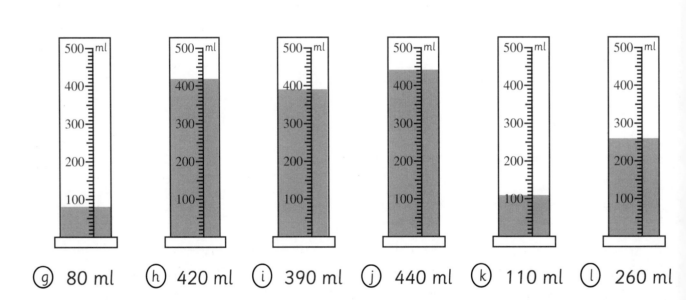

(g) 80 ml   (h) 420 ml   (i) 390 ml   (j) 440 ml   (k) 110 ml   (l) 260 ml

(m) 70 kg   (n) 47 kg   (o) 84 kg

NUMERACY TODAY
© Andrew Brodie *Publications* ✓ www.acblack.com

ABP

Using Measuring Equipment

Name: Date:

To the nearest 10 millilitres, how much water is in each measuring cylinder?

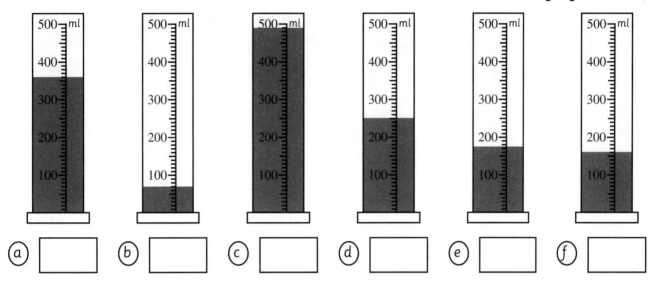

(a) [   ]   (b) [   ]   (c) [   ]   (d) [   ]   (e) [   ]   (f) [   ]

Draw in the water to the measurements given:

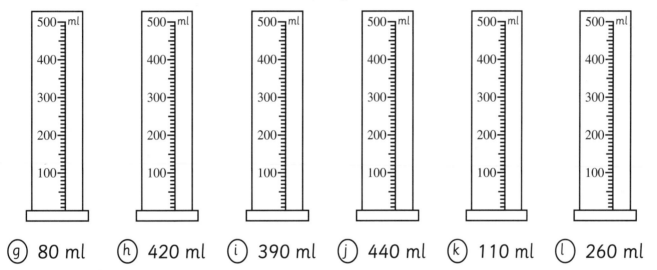

(g) 80 ml   (h) 420 ml   (i) 390 ml   (j) 440 ml   (k) 110 ml   (l) 260 ml

On some bathroom scales, the dial shows through a window.
Three friends, Sarah, Kim and Tarun decided to weigh themselves.
They took turns on the bathroom scales.
What was the approximate weight of each person?

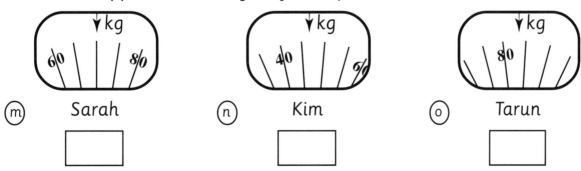

(m) Sarah   (n) Kim   (o) Tarun

[   ]   [   ]   [   ]

All the shapes on sheet 52 have sides which measure to whole or half centimetres.

You could take the opportunity to discuss the shapes shown with the pupils, encouraging them to give detailed definitions:

rectangle: type of quadrilateral where opposite sides are equal and vertices are right angles

square: type of quadrilateral where all sides are equal and vertices are right angles

equilateral triangle: type of triangle where all sides are equal and all angles are equal

regular hexagon: six-sided shape where all sides are equal and all angles are equal

hexagon: six-sided shape (the one shown in question e does have some special features in that the opposite sides and angles are equal but it is not a regular hexagon. It is worth reminding pupils that any six-sided shape is a hexagon)

regular pentagon: five-sided shape where all sides are equal and all angles are equal

The answers to the questions are as follows:

(a) perimeter = 16 cm (sides are 5 cm and 3 cm)   (b) perimeter = 16 cm (sides = 4cm)

(c) perimeter = 9 cm (sides = 3cm)   (d) perimeter = 18 cm (sides = 3cm)

(e) perimeter = 10 cm (sides are 2cm and 1·5cm)   (f) perimeter = 15 cm (sides = 3cm)

g, h and i all have perimeters of 16 cm. Children should notice that these are equal but that the rectangles look different to each other. This will form a good introduction to the concept of shapes with equal perimeters sometimes having different areas.

(j) length of each side = 2 cm

(k) length of each side = 5 cm

Measuring Perimeter

Name: Date:

Measure the sides of each shape, to the nearest half centimetre,
then find the perimeter.

ⓒ Perimeter = [＿＿]

ⓐ Perimeter = [＿＿]

ⓑ Perimeter = [＿＿]

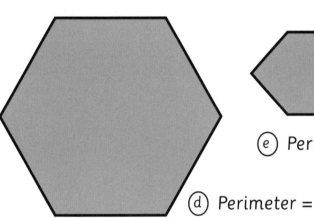

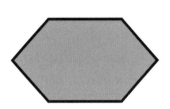

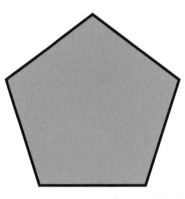

ⓔ Perimeter = [＿＿]

ⓓ Perimeter = [＿＿]

ⓕ Perimeter = [＿＿]

Find the perimeter of each of these rectangles:

ⓗ Perimeter = [＿＿]

ⓖ Perimeter = [＿＿]

ⓘ Perimeter = [＿＿]

What do you notice about the perimeters of these rectangles?

_____

ⓙ If a square has a perimeter of 8 cm what is the length of each side?   [＿＿]

ⓚ If a square has a perimeter of 20 cm what is the length of each side?   [＿＿]
     Draw this square on the back of this sheet.

Finding Area

Pupils will be able to find areas by counting squares. It is most important that they write their answers in square centimetres as shown below:

a 4 cm²   b 12 cm²   c 12 cm²   d ¹/₂ cm²   e ¹/₂ cm²

f 4 cm²   g 16 cm²   h 6 cm²   i 17 cm²   j 28 cm²   k 11 cm²

Questions d and e are provided to show two of the possible ways in which triangles can represent half a square centimetre. Question k should be used for discussion: how do we decide how to count the part squares? Some pupils will notice that the smaller part square will fit together with the larger part to make one whole square centimetre altogether.

Finding Area

Name: Date:

Find the area of each of the shapes and pictures.

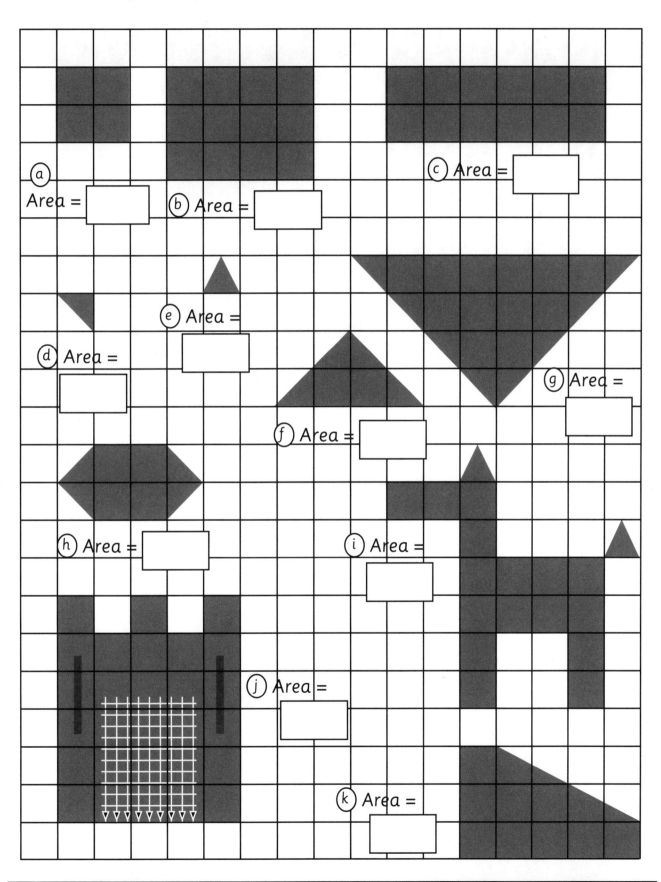

The Calendar

Year 4 pupils need to know the order of the months of the year and the number of days in each month.

Sheet 54 features the well-known rhyme regarding the number of days in each month, together with a calendar showing the year 2000. This provides many opportunities for discussion:

... what is special about the year shown? (The year 2000 has obvious significance but it is also a leap year. Leap years normally occur every four years to make up for the fact that it takes approximately $365\frac{1}{4}$ days for the Earth to travel around the Sun. However, leap years only occur at the turn of a century every four hundred years so the year 1900 was not a leap year.)

... if the pupils have not been told what year the calendar shows, you could ask them if it shows 'this year' - they would need to look at today's date and see if it matched with the day of the week shown <u>and</u> they would need to know if this year is a leap year.

... what day of the week is 11th May? 25th December? 31st July? etc.

... how many Mondays are there in each of the months?

... what day does your birthday fall on this year?

... how many days are there normally in one year?

... how many days are there in the year shown?

... how many months are there in one year?

... how many weeks are there in one year?

... what day of the week would 31st December 1999 be?

... what day of the week would 1st January 2001 be?

Pupils could shade each month carefully in colour, using one colour for months with 31 days, another colour for those with 30 days and another for February. This would encourage them to look at and use the information contained within the rhyme.

The Calendar

Thirty days has September,
April, June and November.
All the rest have thirty-one,
except for February alone,
which has twenty-eight days clear
and twenty-nine in each leap year.

JANUARY						
M	T	W	T	F	S	S
					1	2
3	4	5	6	7	8	9
10	11	12	13	14	15	16
17	18	19	20	21	22	23
24	25	26	27	28	29	30
31						

FEBRUARY						
M	T	W	T	F	S	S
1	2	3	4	5	6	
7	8	9	10	11	12	13
14	15	16	17	18	19	20
21	22	23	24	25	26	27
28	29					

MARCH						
M	T	W	T	F	S	S
	1	2	3	4	5	
6	7	8	9	10	11	12
13	14	15	16	17	18	19
20	21	22	23	24	25	26
27	28	29	30	31		

APRIL						
M	T	W	T	F	S	S
					1	2
3	4	5	6	7	8	9
10	11	12	13	14	15	16
17	18	19	20	21	22	23
24	25	26	27	28	29	30

MAY						
M	T	W	T	F	S	S
1	2	3	4	5	6	7
8	9	10	11	12	13	14
15	16	17	18	19	20	21
22	23	24	25	26	27	28
29	30	31				

JUNE						
M	T	W	T	F	S	S
				1	2	3	4
5	6	7	8	9	10	11
12	13	14	15	16	17	18
19	20	21	22	23	24	25
26	27	28	29	30		

JULY						
M	T	W	T	F	S	S
					1	2
3	4	5	6	7	8	9
10	11	12	13	14	15	16
17	18	19	20	21	22	23
24	25	26	27	28	29	30
31						

AUGUST						
M	T	W	T	F	S	S
1	2	3	4	5	6	
7	8	9	10	11	12	13
14	15	16	17	18	19	20
21	22	23	24	25	26	27
28	29	30	31			

SEPTEMBER						
M	T	W	T	F	S	S
				1	2	3
4	5	6	7	8	9	10
11	12	13	14	15	16	17
18	19	20	21	22	23	24
25	26	27	28	29	30	

OCTOBER						
M	T	W	T	F	S	S
						1
2	3	4	5	6	7	8
9	10	11	12	13	14	15
16	17	18	19	20	21	22
23	24	25	26	27	28	29
30	31					

NOVEMBER						
M	T	W	T	F	S	S
	1	2	3	4	5	
6	7	8	9	10	11	12
13	14	15	16	17	18	19
20	21	22	23	24	25	26
27	28	29	30			

DECEMBER						
M	T	W	T	F	S	S
				1	2	3
4	5	6	7	8	9	10
11	12	13	14	15	16	17
18	19	20	21	22	23	24
25	26	27	28	29	30	31

Symmetrical Reflections (2)

Sheet 55 provides shapes which are parallel to the mirror line. The children need to observe how far away from the mirror line each shape is so that they draw its reflection at an appropriate distance. For questions f and g they will need to measure carefully with a ruler. The answers are as shown below:

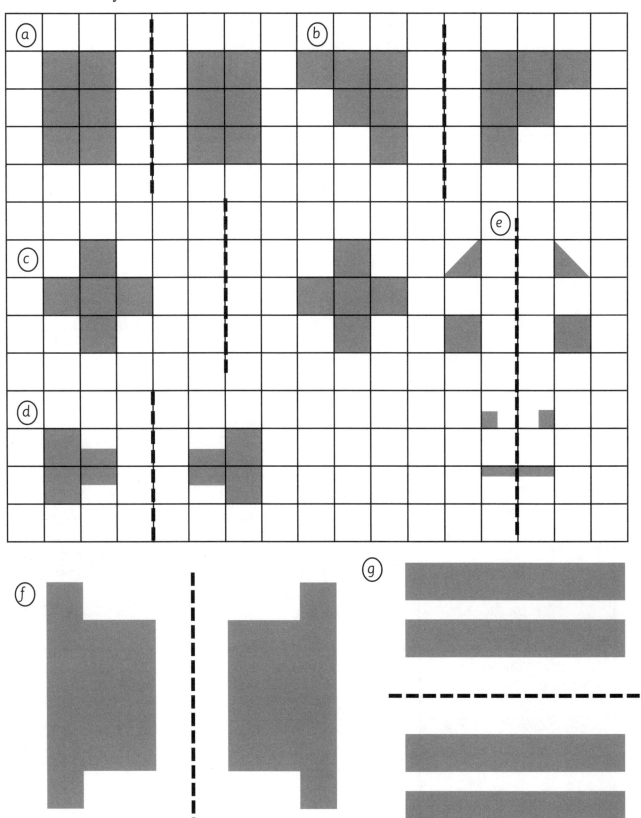

NUMERACY TODAY
© Andrew Brodie *Publications* ✓ www.acblack.com

ABP

Symmetrical Reflections (2)

Name: Date:

Draw the reflection of each of the shapes using the mirror lines shown:

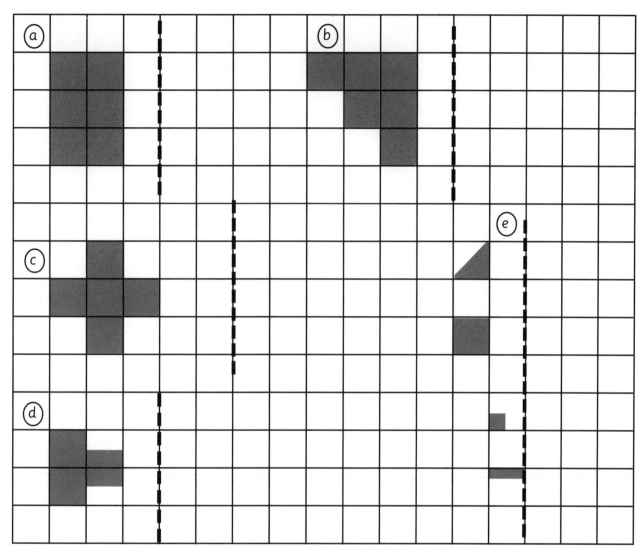

Now try these:

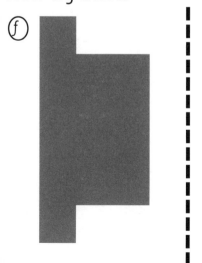

(g)

Coordinates

Sheet 56 provides a development from sheet 36. On sheet 36, pupils are required to find positions of squares marked on a grid. On this sheet there is a similar grid but the children are required to mark points where lines cross, by using their coordinates.

Year 4 pupils need to know:

> … that coordinates are shown as two numbers within brackets and separated by a comma, for example (6,4)

> … that the point (0, 0) is called the origin

> … that coordinates are found by firstly moving across the grid by the number of lines shown in the first part of the coordinate, then moving up the grid by the number of lines shown in the second part. To find the point (6,4) for example, they should start at the origin, then move across to line 6 and up to line 4.

The coordinates given will create the following shape:

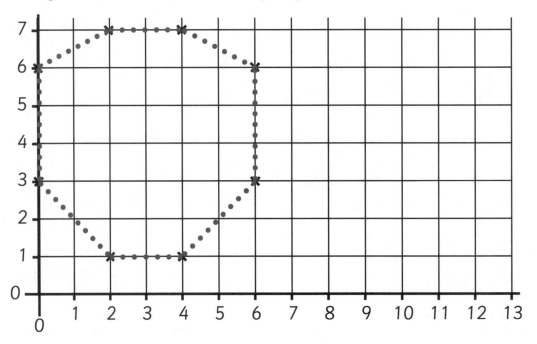

The shape drawn is, of course, an octagon. It is irregular but it does have one line of symmetry.

There is plenty of room left on the grid for pupils to create their own shapes. They could work in pairs where one child prepares a shape then gives coordinates for the other person to mark on the grid.

ABP

Coordinates

Name: Date:

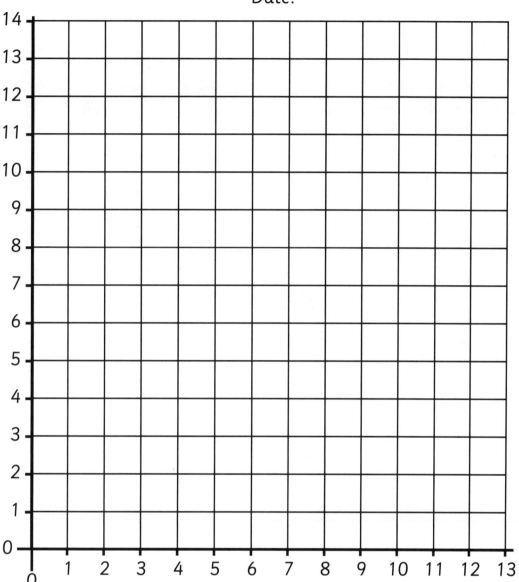

Mark on the grid the points which have these coordinates:

(2,1)   (0,3)   (0,6)   (2,7)   (4,7)   (6,6)   (6,3)   (4,1)

Now use straight lines to join: (2,1) to (0,3)   (0,3) to (0,6)
(0,6) to (2,7)   (2,7) to (4,7)   (4,7) to (6,6)   (6,6) to (6,3)
(6,3) to (4,1) and   (4,1) to (2,1)

What shape have you drawn?   Is it regular?   Is it symmetrical?

Draw some other shapes on the grid, making sure that the vertices are each exactly where two lines cross. State the coordinates of the vertices of the shapes which you draw.

Clock Face and Hands

Sheet 57 provides a clock face and hands which can be photocopied onto card, then cut out to make individual clocks. The face and hands are marked with a cross where holes should be made for attaching the three pieces together with a paper fastener.

You may decide with Year 4 pupils just to attach the hour hand or the minute hand and use the clock face for practice with rotating through specified angles:

The angle between the two positions of the hand is 90°.

The angle between the two positions of the hand is 30°.

The angle between the two positions of the hand is 60°.

You could ask the pupils to start on a specified number then rotate the hand through 60° clockwise - what number is the hand pointing at now? Rotations of 30° or 90° could be made. You could ask the children to rotate the hands by specified angles in an anti-clockwise direction instead. When children are confident they could try rotating the hands through 120°, 150° or 180°.

NUMERACY TODAY
© Andrew Brodie *Publications* ✓ www.acblack.com

ABP

Clock Face and Hands

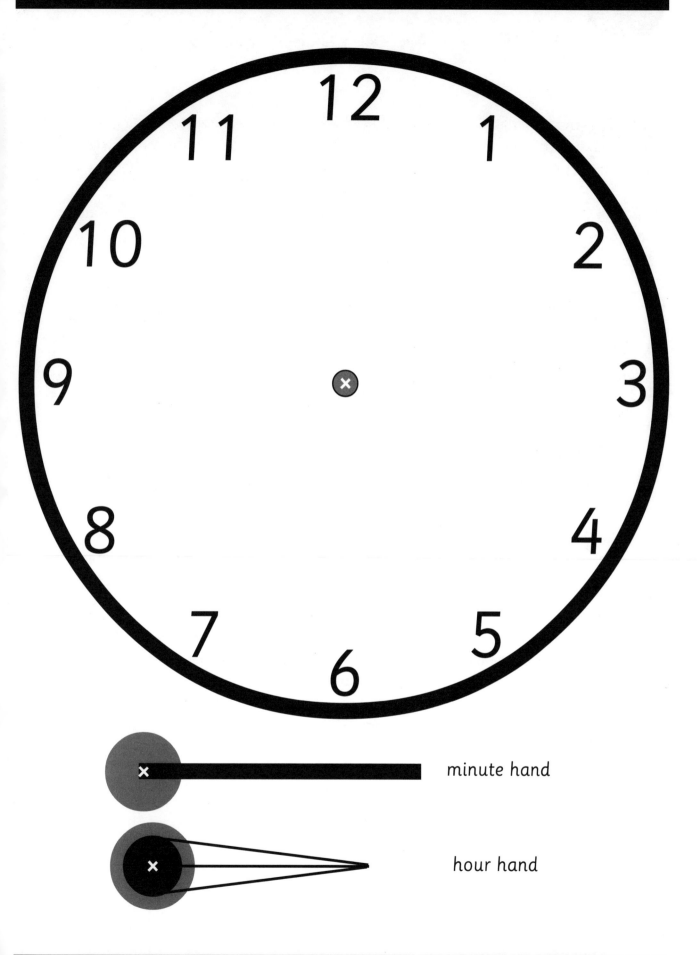

minute hand

hour hand

Two Way Venn Diagram

The Venn Diagram on sheet 58 is a further development from the simple diagram on sheet 40. It can be used in many ways for sorting information and assists children in thinking logically.

For example:

... you could ask the pupils to consider the set of numbers from 1 to 30, sorting them so that multiples of 3 are in one circle and multiples of 4 are in the other. All numbers which are left over are placed outside the circles as they are 'not multiples of 3 or 4'.

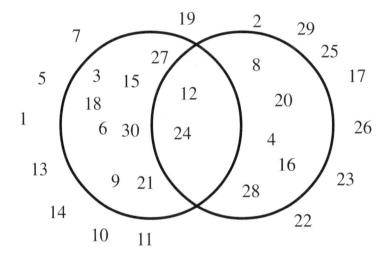

Sorting the numbers is this way shows the numbers which are multiples of both three and four as they are the ones which are positioned within both circles.

... you could ask the pupils to sort a set of shapes which you provide. They could be sorted so that those which include at least one right angle go into one circle and those which are regular (ie all sides are equal in length) go into the other circle.

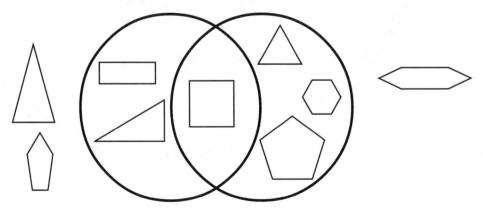

ABP

Two Way Venn Diagram

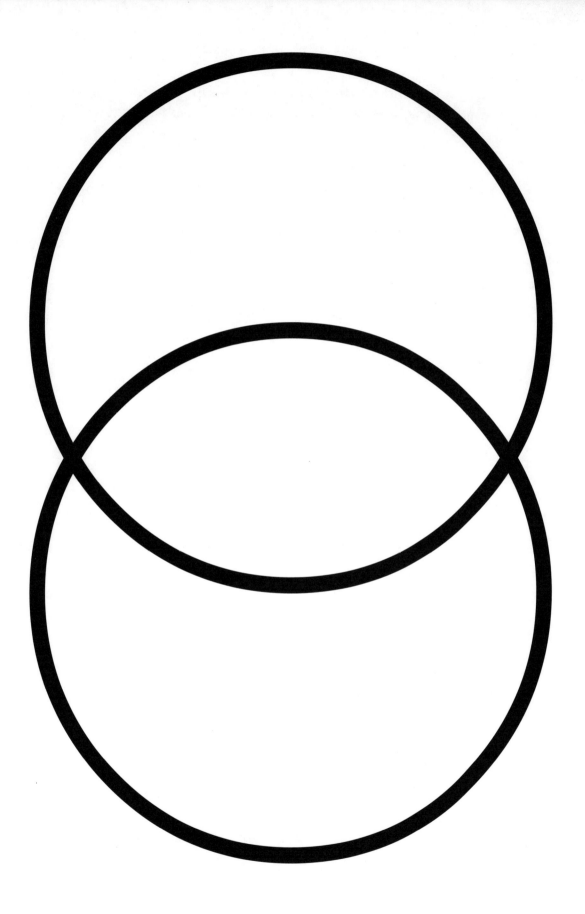

Two Way Carroll Diagram

Sheet 59 provides a further development from the simple Carroll diagram on sheet 39 and, like the Venn diagram helps to develop children's logical thinking.

Examples:

… you could ask the children to sort a set of numbers from 1 to 30 into multiples of 3 and multiples of 4, as in the example with the Venn diagram:

	multiples of three	not multiples of three
multiples of four	12 24	20 28 8 4 16
not multiples of four	3 15 18 27 6 30 9 21	19 5 17 29 22 7 14 2 13 10 26 23 11 25 1

It is interesting to compare the sorting onto the Carroll diagram to that onto the Venn diagram.

… you could ask the children to sort the set of numbers from 1 to 30 into numbers which are even and numbers which are greater than 20:

	even	not even
> 20	30 28 26 24 22	25 21 23 29 27
not > 20	12 20 6 8 2 4 14 16 18 10	3 15 5 1 9 17 7 11 13 19

Two Way Carroll Diagram

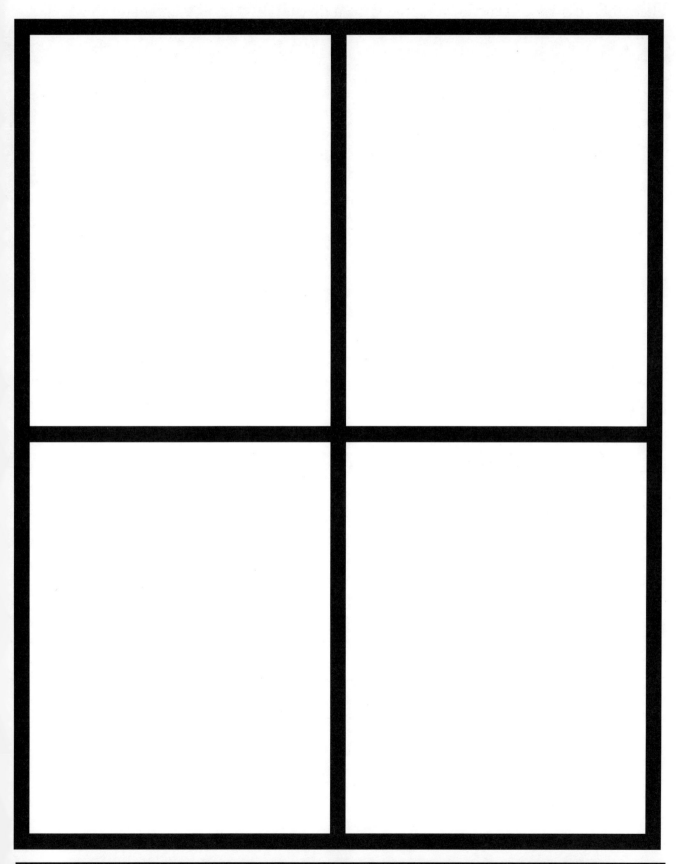

Handling Data: Eggs

This sheet provides useful practice of the six times table as well as showing two different types of chart. The charts provide many opportunities for discussion:

… on which day of the week was the shop closed?

… on which day were most eggs sold?

… on which day were the fewest eggs sold?

… how many more boxes were sold on Saturday than Friday?

… why do you think so many boxes of eggs were sold on Saturday?
   (Note: there is no 'right' answer to this question. Children will offer a
      variety of interesting answers, all of which could be correct so long
      as they make sense.)

… how many boxes of eggs were sold altogether during this week?

After working out the answers to the questions at the bottom of the sheet, pupils could be asked how many individual eggs were sold altogether during the week. They could go on to making a bar chart as shown below:

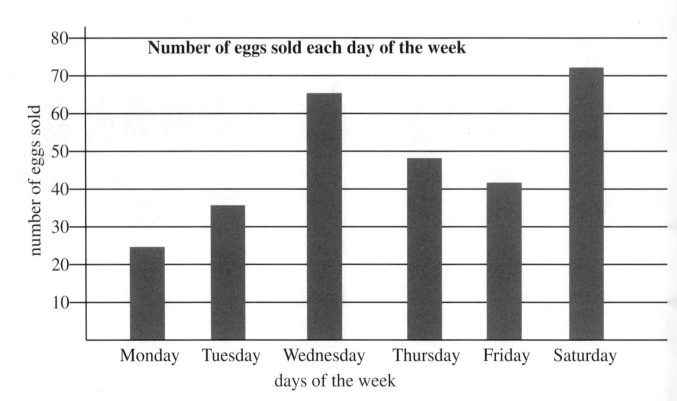

Name: Date:

Mr Lee sells eggs in his shop. The eggs are in boxes of six. One week he made a tally chart of the boxes he sold:

Monday	Tuesday	Wednesday	Thursday	Friday	Saturday
||||	₩T |	₩T ₩T |	₩T |||	₩T ||	₩T ₩T ||

Mr Lee's daughter, Jo, decided to make a pictogram showing how many boxes of eggs were sold but she didn't finish it. Finish the pictogram for her by drawing eggs. Remember that each egg-picture represents 1 box of eggs.

Boxes of eggs sold last week    = 1 box of 6 eggs

Monday ●●●●

Tuesday

Wednesday

Thursday

Friday

Saturday

Jo thought it would be interesting to find out how many individual eggs were sold. She realised that four boxes of eggs were sold on Monday. Each box holds six eggs. Four boxes of six makes twenty-four eggs altogether.

How many eggs were sold each day?

Monday: 4 boxes of 6 = 24   Tuesday:

Wednesday: Thursday:

Friday: Saturday:

Fraction Cards

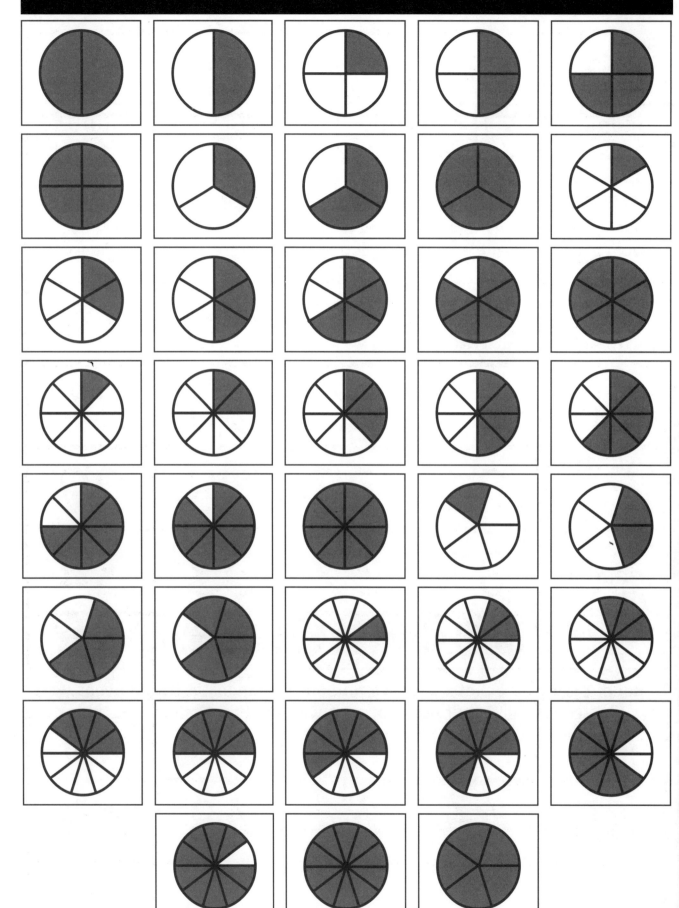

Number Flashcards: 0 to 50

0	1	2	3	4
5	6	7	8	9
10	11	12	13	14
15	16	17	18	19
20	21	22	23	24
25	26	27	28	29
30	31	32	33	34
35	36	37	38	39
40	41	42	43	44
45	46	47	48	49
50	+	−	X	÷

ABP

NUMERACY TODAY
© Andrew Brodie *Publications* ✓ www.acblack.com

ABP

Multiplication and Division Tables

Name:

0 x 2 = 0	0 ÷ 2 = 0	0 x 3 = 0	0 ÷ 3 = 0	0 x 4 = 0	0 ÷ 4 = 0
1 x 2 = 2	2 ÷ 2 = 1	1 x 3 = 3	3 ÷ 3 = 1	1 x 4 = 4	4 ÷ 4 = 1
2 x 2 = 4	4 ÷ 2 = 2	2 x 3 = 6	6 ÷ 3 = 2	2 x 4 = 8	8 ÷ 4 = 2
3 x 2 = 6	6 ÷ 2 = 3	3 x 3 = 9	9 ÷ 3 = 3	3 x 4 = 12	12 ÷ 4 = 3
4 x 2 = 8	8 ÷ 2 = 4	4 x 3 = 12	12 ÷ 3 = 4	4 x 4 = 16	16 ÷ 4 = 4
5 x 2 = 10	10 ÷ 2 = 5	5 x 3 = 15	15 ÷ 3 = 5	5 x 4 = 20	20 ÷ 4 = 5
6 x 2 = 12	12 ÷ 2 = 6	6 x 3 = 18	18 ÷ 3 = 6	6 x 4 = 24	24 ÷ 4 = 6
7 x 2 = 14	14 ÷ 2 = 7	7 x 3 = 21	21 ÷ 3 = 7	7 x 4 = 28	28 ÷ 4 = 7
8 x 2 = 16	16 ÷ 2 = 8	8 x 3 = 24	24 ÷ 3 = 8	8 x 4 = 32	32 ÷ 4 = 8
9 x 2 = 18	18 ÷ 2 = 9	9 x 3 = 27	27 ÷ 3 = 9	9 x 4 = 36	36 ÷ 4 = 9
10 x 2 = 20	20 ÷ 2 =10	10 x 3 = 30	30 ÷ 3 =10	10 x 4 = 40	40 ÷ 4 =10
0 x 5 = 0	0 ÷ 5 = 0	0 x 6 = 0	0 ÷ 6 = 0	0 x 7 = 0	0 ÷ 7 = 0
1 x 5 = 5	5 ÷ 5 = 1	1 x 6 = 6	6 ÷ 6 = 1	1 x 7 = 7	7 ÷ 7 = 1
2 x 5 = 10	10 ÷ 5 = 2	2 x 6 = 12	12 ÷ 6 = 2	2 x 7 = 14	14 ÷ 7 = 2
3 x 5 = 15	15 ÷ 5 = 3	3 x 6 = 18	18 ÷ 6 = 3	3 x 7 = 21	21 ÷ 7 = 3
4 x 5 = 20	20 ÷ 5 = 4	4 x 6 = 24	24 ÷ 6 = 4	4 x 7 = 28	28 ÷ 7 = 4
5 x 5 = 25	25 ÷ 5 = 5	5 x 6 = 30	30 ÷ 6 = 5	5 x 7 = 35	35 ÷ 7 = 5
6 x 5 = 30	30 ÷ 5 = 6	6 x 6 = 36	36 ÷ 6 = 6	6 x 7 = 42	42 ÷ 7 = 6
7 x 5 = 35	35 ÷ 5 = 7	7 x 6 = 42	42 ÷ 6 = 7	7 x 7 = 49	49 ÷ 7 = 7
8 x 5 = 40	40 ÷ 5 = 8	8 x 6 = 48	48 ÷ 6 = 8	8 x 7 = 56	56 ÷ 7 = 8
9 x 5 = 45	45 ÷ 5 = 9	9 x 6 = 54	54 ÷ 6 = 9	9 x 7 = 63	63 ÷ 7 = 9
10 x 5 = 50	50 ÷ 5 =10	10 x 6 = 60	60 ÷ 6 =10	10 x 7 = 70	70 ÷ 7 =10
0 x 8 = 0	0 ÷ 8 = 0	0 x 9 = 0	0 ÷ 9 = 0	0 x 10 = 0	0 ÷ 10 = 0
1 x 8 = 8	8 ÷ 8 = 1	1 x 9 = 9	9 ÷ 9 = 1	1 x 10 = 10	10 ÷ 10 = 1
2 x 8 = 16	16 ÷ 8 = 2	2 x 9 = 18	18 ÷ 9 = 2	2 x 10 = 20	20 ÷ 10 = 2
3 x 8 = 24	24 ÷ 8 = 3	3 x 9 = 27	27 ÷ 9 = 3	3 x 10 = 30	30 ÷ 10 = 3
4 x 8 = 32	32 ÷ 8 = 4	4 x 9 = 36	36 ÷ 9 = 4	4 x 10 = 40	40 ÷ 10 = 4
5 x 8 = 40	40 ÷ 8 = 5	5 x 9 = 45	45 ÷ 9 = 5	5 x 10 = 50	50 ÷ 10 = 5
6 x 8 = 48	48 ÷ 8 = 6	6 x 9 = 54	54 ÷ 9 = 6	6 x 10 = 60	60 ÷ 10 = 6
7 x 8 = 56	56 ÷ 8 = 7	7 x 9 = 63	63 ÷ 9 = 7	7 x 10 = 70	70 ÷ 10 = 7
8 x 8 = 64	64 ÷ 8 = 8	8 x 9 = 72	72 ÷ 9 = 8	8 x 10 = 80	80 ÷ 10 = 8
9 x 8 = 72	72 ÷ 8 = 9	9 x 9 = 81	81 ÷ 9 = 9	9 x 10 = 90	90 ÷ 10 = 9
10 x 8 = 80	80 ÷ 8 =10	10 x 9 = 90	90 ÷ 9 =10	10 x 10 =100	100 ÷ 10 =10

Numeracy Today is published by Andrew Brodie Publications.
Andrew Brodie Publications publish a range of educational workbooks for children, available through bookstores.

NUMERACY TODAY
© Andrew Brodie *Publications* ✓ www.acblack.com

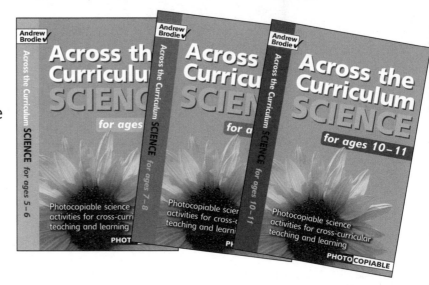
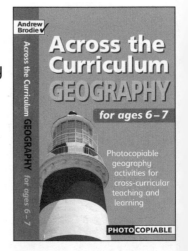
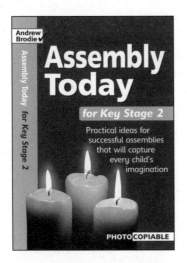